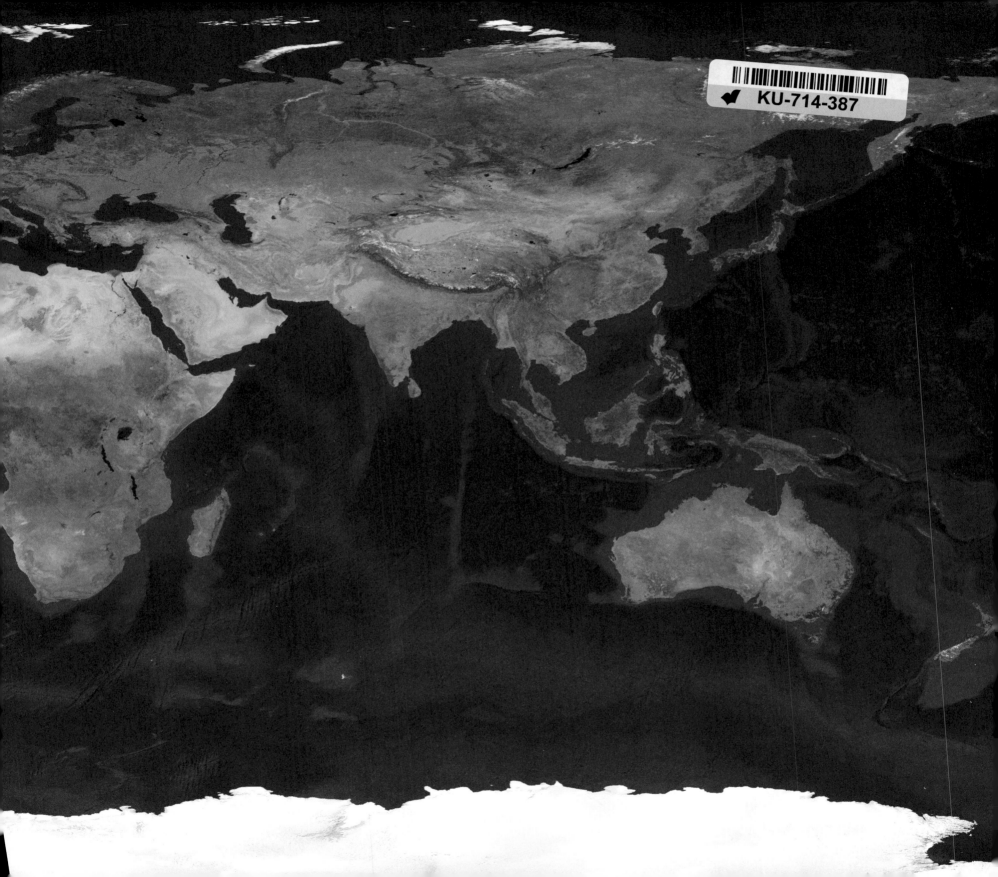

KU-714-387

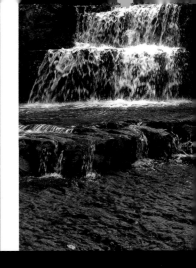

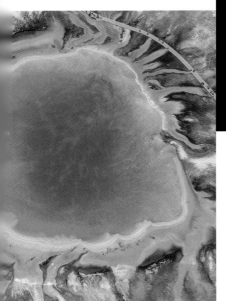

INCREDIBLE EARTH

OUR PLANET'S MOST SPECTACULAR GEOGRAPHY

STEWART MCPHERSON

Don Hanson Charitable Foundation
Linden House, Linden Close, Tunbridge Wells, Kent TN4 8HH, United Kingdom
www.donhansoncharitablefoundation.org

INCREDIBLE EARTH *The World's Most Spectacular Geography*
ISBN 978-1-913631-02-4

Copyright © Don Hanson Charitable Foundation

All rights reserved. First printed June, 2020
Printed in Slovenia on behalf of Latitude Press Limited

Reproduction or translation of any part of this book, except for short excerpts used in reviews, without the written permission of the publisher is unlawful. Requests for permission to reproduce parts of this work, or for additional information, should be addressed to the publisher.

Sincere thanks to Dr. Robert Irving for contributing text and editing this work.

Dedicated to my friend Simon Leary for his passion for the world,
and for supporting so many causes to make this planet a better place.

**Printed on Forest Stewardship
Council approved paper**

MIX
Paper from
responsible sources
FSC® C106600

Special Thanks to

The Don Hanson Charitable Foundation

Working to provide knowledge and inspire awareness about nature, science and the conservation of our world.

One copy of this book has been donated to each of 20,000 primary schools across the United Kingdom and her Overseas Territories, and also 4,000 primary schools across Australia.

www.donhansoncharitablefoundation.org   www.hansonbox.org

CONTENTS

G.K. Chesterton: *'We are perishing for want of wonder, not for want of wonders'.*

OUR INCREDIBLE EARTH

For thousands of years, human civilisations believed that our world was the centre of the Universe, which consisted only of those planets visible with the naked eye and an outlying sphere of fixed stars.

Four hundred years of telescopic observations and scientific study has changed our understanding radically.

We now know that Earth is 12,756 km in diameter, positioned as the third planet from the Sun (at a distance of approximately of 149.6 million km), and is traveling through space at nearly 1.6 million km per hour.

Our world is one of eight planets and many smaller objects that make up the Solar System orbiting the Sun.

We know our Sun is one of over 8.8 billion other stars that make up the Milky Way Galaxy. The number of planets in the Galaxy is unknown, but thousand of our nearest stars have been observed to have their own systems of orbiting planets.

Lastly, astronomers believe that the Milky Way is just one of an estimated one to two trillion galaxies in the observable universe.

Radiometric dating techniques indicate that our Earth formed around 4.54 billion years ago. Ever since, the surface of our planet has continually changed and adjusted, slowly giving rise to the world we know today.

All the while, Earth continued to orbit the Sun, spinning on its Axis as the Eons and Ages have passed.

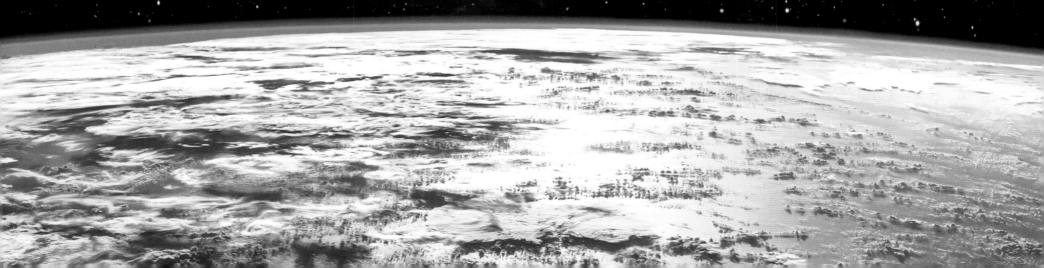

THE MAKING OF EARTH

The formation of Planet Earth can be divided into four great Eons of geological time:

Hadean Eon (4.5-4.0 billion years ago): following the formation of the Sun, debris was pulled together under the force of its own gravity. It first formed a protoplanetary disk, and then aggregated together as a sphere. Temperatures on the young planet's surface were extremely hot, with frequent volcanic activity. Slowly Earth began to cool as it radiated heat. The molten rock solidified and water vapour began to condense. Gradually, the earliest land and oceans formed, but there was no life on Earth.

Archean Eon (4.0-2.5 billion years ago): chemicals in the Earth's oceans react and diversify as minerals. Replicating molecules emerged and gave rise to bacteria-like Prokaryotes, the planet's first form of life.

Proterozoic Eon (2.5 billion - 541 million years ago): Eukaryotes (whose cells have a nucleus enclosed within a membrane) emerged, and their more complex structure allowed multicellular organisms to evolve. Bacteria began producing oxygen, allowing plants, animals and early forms of fungi to develop. Massive temperature fluctuations occurred, including "Snowball Earth" periods, during which the whole planet was subjected to sub-zero temperatures. At certain points, it appeared that life may be entirely extinguished, but extreme forms of life survived.

Phanerozoic Eon (541 million years ago - present): complex life emerged, including vertebrate animals. During the 'Cambrian explosion', tens of millions of species evolved, diversified and became extinct, slowly giving rise to the lineages of life that exist today. After several global mass extinction events, mammals became dominant across much of the world, finally giving rise to the evolution of hominids, including our species, *Homo sapiens*.

INCREDIBLE EARTH

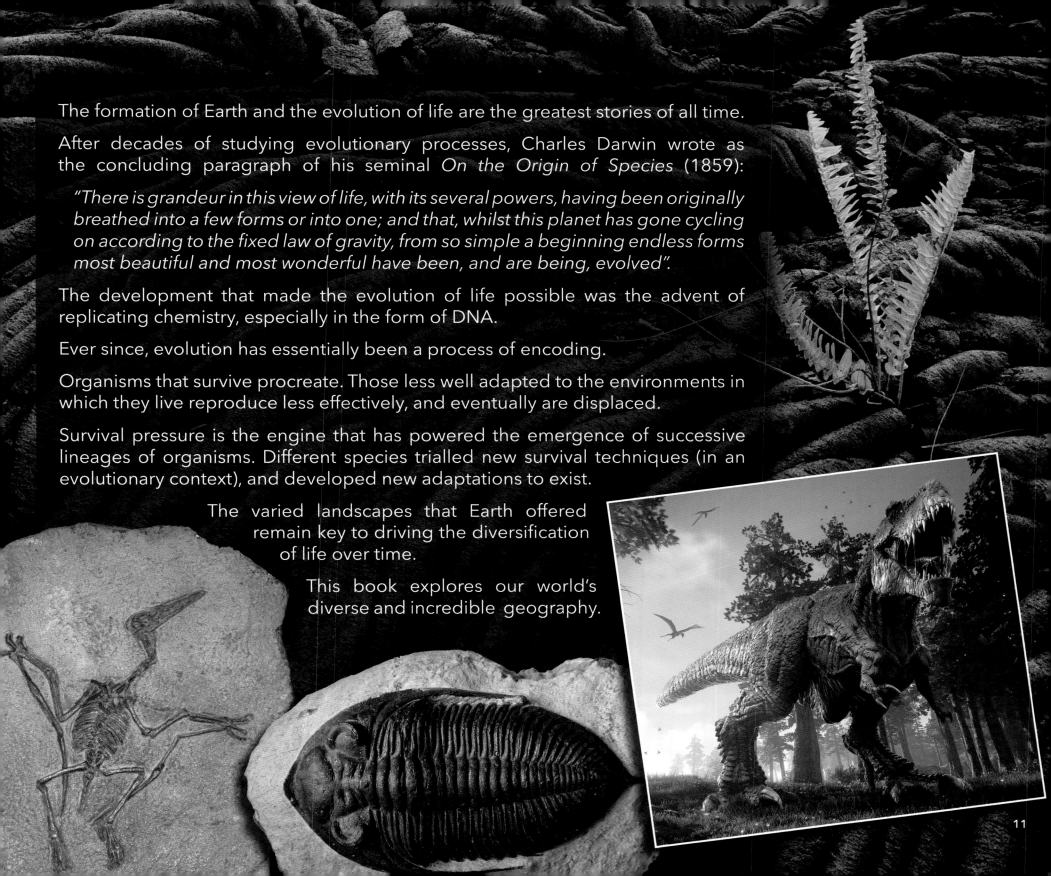

The formation of Earth and the evolution of life are the greatest stories of all time.

After decades of studying evolutionary processes, Charles Darwin wrote as the concluding paragraph of his seminal *On the Origin of Species* (1859):

"There is grandeur in this view of life, with its several powers, having been originally breathed into a few forms or into one; and that, whilst this planet has gone cycling on according to the fixed law of gravity, from so simple a beginning endless forms most beautiful and most wonderful have been, and are being, evolved".

The development that made the evolution of life possible was the advent of replicating chemistry, especially in the form of DNA.

Ever since, evolution has essentially been a process of encoding.

Organisms that survive procreate. Those less well adapted to the environments in which they live reproduce less effectively, and eventually are displaced.

Survival pressure is the engine that has powered the emergence of successive lineages of organisms. Different species trialled new survival techniques (in an evolutionary context), and developed new adaptations to exist.

The varied landscapes that Earth offered remain key to driving the diversification of life over time.

This book explores our world's diverse and incredible geography.

STRUCTURE OF EARTH

Planet Earth consists of several layers that differ in density and composition:

The **crust** is the outer (and thinnest) layer of the planet's structure. It varies in thickness from 5-7 km beneath the oceans, to 10-75 km under the continents.

Below the crust is the **mantle**, which consists of upper and lower layers that together, are around 2,900 km thick. The mantle consists dense, solid rock, but over geological time, may behave as a viscous fluid.

Beneath the mantle is the **core**, which is thought to be composed mostly of liquid iron, nickel and sulphur. The core consists of two parts: 2,250 km of outer core and 1,220 km of inner core.

The inner core has an incredibly high temperature of 4,400 to 6,000°C. The iron within the core is responsible for creating the Earth's magnetic field, and the North and South magnetic poles.

CRUST

UPPER MANTLE

LOWER MANTLE

OUTER CORE

INNER CORE

 # GEOLOGICAL TIME

Understanding the immensity of the universe's dimensions of time and space is very difficult.

The Earth is believed to have formed about 4.5 billion years ago, when gravity pulled circulating gas and dust into an ever-closer sphere and the third planet from the Sun was created.

This is regarded as the start of Geological Time on Earth, which is measured in huge units corresponding to the formation of different geological strata or rocky layers.

The largest time-units are eons (lasting thousands of millions of years), then eras, periods and epochs (which last tens of millions of years).

This system was devised by geologists to understand Earth's history, and to make sense of the age of different rock types. It was not until the scientific study of fossils began that their age was linked with the type of rock strata they were found within.

Geologists can now use radio-carbon dating to provide accurate ages for many fossils.

FACTS ABOUT EARTH

HIGHEST MOUNTAIN ON EARTH

Mount Everest, on the border between Nepal and Tibet in the Himalaya mountain range, is famed as the world's highest mountain at 8,848 m above sea level. However, the island of Mauna Kea (one of the Hawaiian islands in the Pacific) sits on top of a submarine mountain, so it's true height is about 10,000 m from the sea floor.

DEEPEST PART OF THE OCEANS

The Challenger Deep is an area of the Mariana Trench in the western Pacific Ocean. It reaches 10,928 m below sea level. The Trench itself is crescent-shaped, being 2,550 km long and about 69 km wide.

HOTTEST PLACE ON EARTH

54°C has been measured in Death Valley, California and also at Mitribah, Kuwait. Dallol in Ethiopia is the hottest inhabited place, having an annual average temperature of 34.4°C.

DRIEST PLACE ON EARTH

Chile's Atacama Desert has the lowest average annual rainfall of just 15 mm, but parts of Antarctica may receive no precipitation for years.

COLDEST PLACE ON EARTH

The coldest inhabited place on Earth is Eureka, Nunavut in northern Canada with an average annual temperature of -19.7°C. However, Oymymakon in the Sakha Republic (Russian Federation) has a mean monthly temperature in January of -46.4°C.

The South Pole and other uninhabited places in Antarctica experience even colder temperatures. In 1983, -89.2°C was recorded at Vostok Station, Antarctica.

LARGEST VOLCANO ON EARTH

Several volcanoes compete for this accolade.

The Tamu Massif is the world's largest volcano complex, and covers over 553,000 km² in the north-western Pacific (below sea level).

Mauna Kea (see highest mountain section) has the greatest height from base to summit, while Ojos del Salado in the Andes has the highest summit elevation above sea level, at 6,839 m.

LARGEST METEORITE IMPACT CRATER ON EARTH

The largest known meteorite impact crater on Earth is the Vredefort Crater, which has a radius over 190 km. It is located in Free State, South Africa, and was created around 2 billion years ago.

The 81 km wide Chicxulub Crater in Mexico's Yucatan Peninsula, is evidence of another massive impact event that took place 65 million and caused (or contributed to) the extinction of the dinosaurs.

AURORAS

The Auroras are a dazzling display of ethereal coloured lights which appear in the night sky of polar regions. The displays seen around the North Pole are known as the Aurora Borealis (or Northern Lights) while those around the South Pole are known as the Aurora Australis (Southern Lights).

The amazing light patterns form high in the Earth's atmosphere at altitudes of between 80 to 320 km.

Auroras occur when charged particles from the sun are carried to our planet by the solar wind, and become trapped in the Earth's magnetic field. The particles ionise oxygen and nitrogen molecules in the upper atmosphere, creating light.

For the best places to see this heavenly light show, you need to be at a latitude above 55° and somewhere clear of light pollution (so in the countryside, on the coast or at sea, rather than in a town or city).

Displays may occur on any dark night, with long winter nights being good but not necessarily the best time. Near the equinoxes in March and September are when the Earth's magnetic field lets more particles interact with the atmosphere, so these are usually optimal times to observe auroras.

Not surprisingly, auroras figure prominently in the mythology and legends of many indigenous cultures, and have long carried spiritual significance.

Native peoples of Greenland, traditionally believe the 'sky lights' to be the spirits of children that died at birth. Their playful souls are said to be dancing in the heavens.

The ancient Greeks believed the phenomenon to be the deity Aurora, sister of Helios and Seline, the sun and moon. They held that Aurora raced across the early morning sky in her multi-coloured chariot to alert her siblings to the dawning of a new day.

The Romans held similar beliefs, and worshipped Aurora, the goddess of dawn, who travelled from east to west announcing the coming of the sun. It is from these Greek and Roman origins that the phenomenon's name was adopted.

Auroras displays differ in their patterns and rhythm. They may be green, yellow, blue, pink, red, purple, or combinations of these colours.

CHAIN LIGHTNING

Lightning plays an extremely important role in nurturing life on Earth.

Lightning strikes oxidise nitrogen in the air, fixing it as nitrates which are deposited by rain. This process fertilises the growth of plants and other organisms.

Most lightning strikes occur singly, however, under rare circumstances, multiple lightning strikes can be produced from a cloud as chain lightning.

One of the best examples of repeated lightning occurs at Lake Maracaibo in Venezuela, South America, where the phenomenon is called Catatumbo lightning (shown opposite).

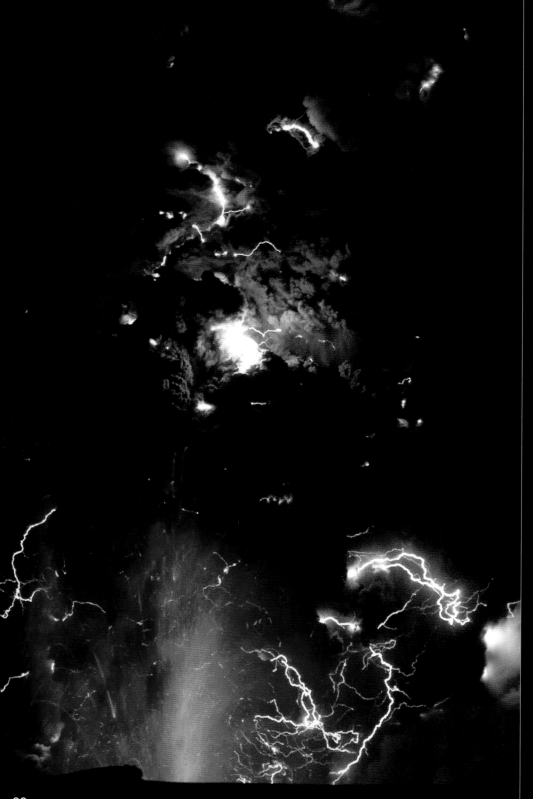

In a Catatumbo lightning storm, hundreds of lightning strikes may happen one after another, illuminating the sky. Locals call the phenomenon the 'everlasting storm'.

The lightning may illuminate the night sky for up to nine hours at a time, with lightning strikes taking place as frequently as every two seconds.

At Lake Maracaibo, Catatumbo lightning takes place on as many as 200 nights each year, generating over one million lightning strikes annually. This amazing spectacle may be visible in the night sky from as far away as 400 km!

Erupting volcanoes have been known to generate similar high-frequency lightning storms as a result of the friction that rapidly rising plumes of hot air and ash generate. The lightning often circles the ash cloud, discharging the electricity which the friction generates.

Although not lightning, a weather phenomenon called St. Elmo's fire can appear similar. This is a luminous plasma created by a corona discharge from a sharp or pointed object in a strong electric field in the atmosphere (such as those generated by thunderstorms or volcanic eruption).

The nitrogen and oxygen in the Earth's atmosphere cause St. Elmo's fire to fluoresce with blue or violet light, and it often takes the form of little, electricity-like strikes and flashes. Often it is accompanied by a buzzing sound or loud hiss.

St. Elmo's fire can occur on the exterior of airplane windows, and in the rigging of ships during storms. For hundreds of years, sailors viewed the phenomenon with awe and took it to be a good omen!

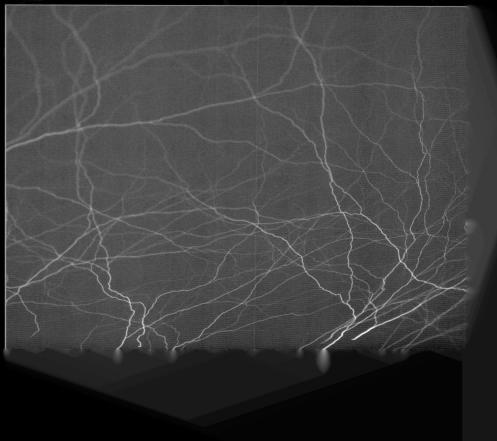

ANTELOPE CANYON

Antelope Canyon is a unique 'slot canyon' that occurs east of the city of Page, in Navajo Nation lands in Arizona, USA.

It has been formed by the gradual, natural erosion of the Navajo sandstone by rainwater, particularly at times of floods. Downpours falling on the surrounding countryside seep through cracks in the rock and can quickly become fast-flowing torrents. Picking up grains of sand in suspension, the water has an abrasive effect on the walls of the canyon, resulting in smoothed curves and sculptural, wavy formations.

Around midday during the summer, shafts of sunlight enter sections of Antelope Canyon, and illuminate the beautiful natural colours and strata of the sandstone.

Since the canyon is so narrow and its path often curved, the illuminated chambers glow orange, pink, red and light purple, and contrast with the rock textures and shadows.

At some places, sand may slowly cascade down rock ledges, resembling waterfalls.

Despite its beauty, Antelope Canyon is prone to flash flooding, and several tourists have been stranded on ledges, and forced to wait for waters to recede.

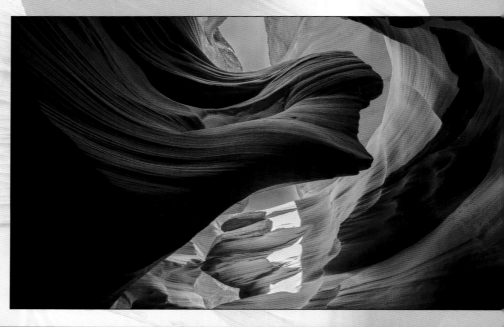

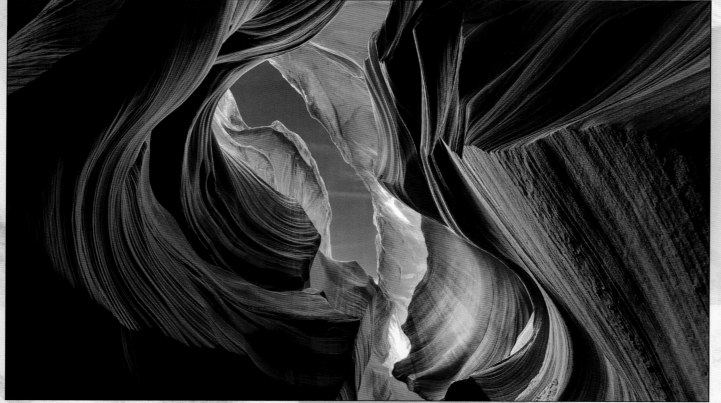

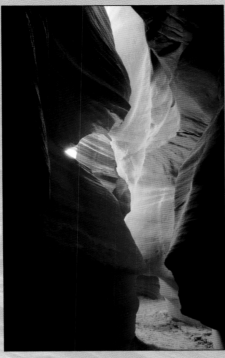

ANTELOPE CANYON

INCREDIBLE EARTH

BASALT COLUMNS

Basalt columns are among the world's most dramatic igneous rocks formations.

More than 90% of all volcanic rock on Earth consists of basalt. There are many different forms of basalt that differ as a result of the elements they contain, and the speed at which the liquid basalt cooled and solidified.

In order to form polygonal columns (as shown here), the cooling process must be slow. The extremely hard-wearing columns may display a hexagonal (6-sided) shape, but they may have any number of sides, from 3 to 9. The gaps between the columns are where the rock has contracted and fractured as it cooled.

The Giant's Causeway on the coast of County Antrim in Northern Ireland is one of the world's most spectacular examples of columnar basalt formations (page 31). It is recognised as both a World Heritage Site and a National Nature Reserve, and received over 1 million visitors in 2018!

The tops of the Giant's Causeway columns form stepping stones that disappear into the sea. Legend has it that the columns once formed a causeway which went all the way across to the island of Staffa in south-west Scotland and were built by the Irish giant Finn MacCool. It was his way of getting across to Scotland in order to defeat his rival, the giant Benandonner. Whether he managed to do this or not depends on whether you're Irish or Scots!

The basaltic columns of the Giant's Causeway re-emerge on the uninhabited island of Staffa in the Inner Hebrides. The island is best known for Fingal's Cave, shown on the right in the photo below.

Fingal's Cave has remarkable acoustic qualities, producing some eerie echoes. This 'music of the sea' is said to have enthused Felix Mendelssohn to write part of his Hebridean overture following his visit to the cave in 1829.

The island of Pohnpei in the western Pacific Ocean, is home to the ruined city of Nan Madol.

This ancient city has been described as one of the world's great archaeological enigmas, and one of the least known wonders of the world.

The city consists of almost 100 man-made islands built within a lagoon. Massive basaltic columns were used to construct buildings on many of the islands. The columns came from a volcanic plug nearby.

The effort to quarry and transport the thousands of columns to build the city is almost incomprehensible, especially without modern mechanised technology.

Up to 1,000 people inhabited Nan Madol for over 400 years. But the site was deserted after 1628, when it was overrun by another ruler. Lack of food and freshwater may also have contributed to the city's downfall.

BIOLUMINESCENT WATERS

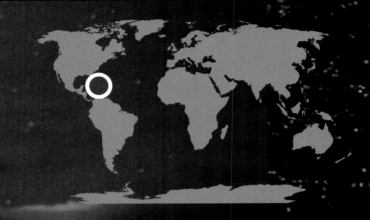

Imagine wandering along a sandy beach at night with stars twinkling in the sky above. Then, you look down and see thousands of pin-pricks of light in the waves and on the wet sand of the beach!

This phenomenon is known as marine bioluminescence, and it occurs in many places around the world. The best beach to witness it is located in Mosquito Bay, on the small island of Vieques, off the east coast of Puerto Rico.

The pin-pricks of light come from thousands of minute marine creatures called dinoflagellates, which create the bioluminescence when they are disturbed.

The glow is a defence mechanism. If a predator consumes the dinoflagellates, it becomes illuminated by the glow the dinoflagellates produce. The predator therefore becomes conspicuous to its enemies. To avoid this risk, most animals leave the dinoflagellates alone.

Bioluminescence is defined as the production and emission of light by a living organism. The glow is produced by a chemical reaction between a substance called luciferin and an enzyme called luciferase.

The enzyme catalyses the oxidation of the luciferin and a blue-coloured light is produced as a result.

Many deep-sea fish use the same process to produce light to lure prey towards them in the darkness. Other species of fish are able to flash their lights on and off as a means of communication.

A few species of squid are able to produce pockets of bioluminescent light on their undersides, which break up their outlines to any predators viewing them from below.

As disturbance triggers the dinoflagellates to emit their beautiful blue glow, dolphins, fish and boats moving in the waters of Mosquito Bay are trailed with sparkling blue light, and the crashing waves cause an eerie glow to spread along the length of the beach.

As the waves wash dinoflagellates onto the sand, you can paint the beach with their glow (see page 37).

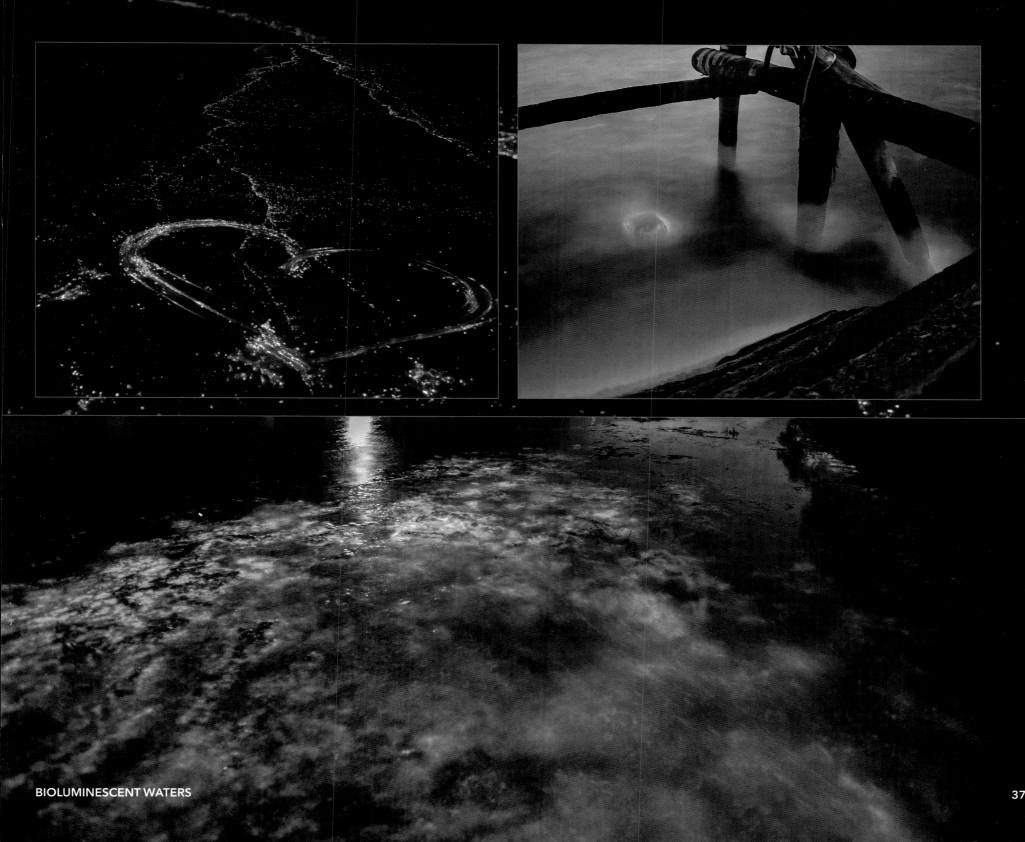

BIOLUMINESCENT WATERS

BARRIER REEFS

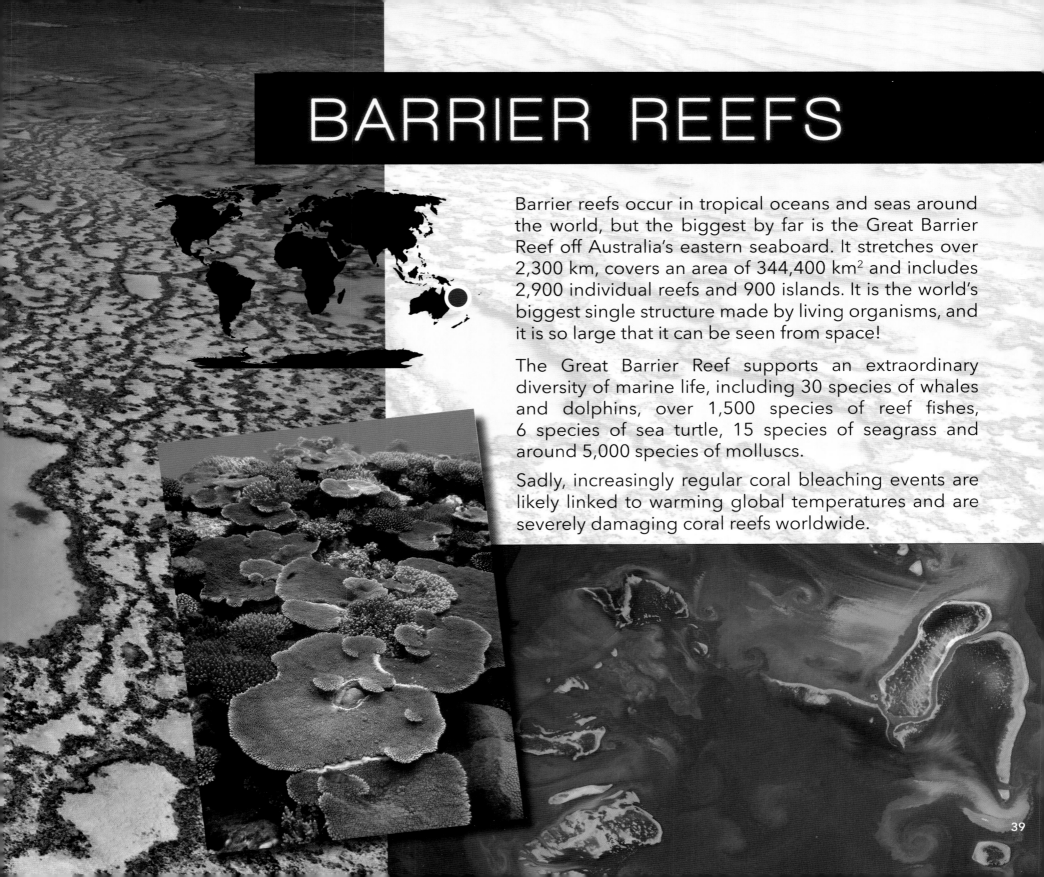

Barrier reefs occur in tropical oceans and seas around the world, but the biggest by far is the Great Barrier Reef off Australia's eastern seaboard. It stretches over 2,300 km, covers an area of 344,400 km^2 and includes 2,900 individual reefs and 900 islands. It is the world's biggest single structure made by living organisms, and it is so large that it can be seen from space!

The Great Barrier Reef supports an extraordinary diversity of marine life, including 30 species of whales and dolphins, over 1,500 species of reef fishes, 6 species of sea turtle, 15 species of seagrass and around 5,000 species of molluscs.

Sadly, increasingly regular coral bleaching events are likely linked to warming global temperatures and are severely damaging coral reefs worldwide.

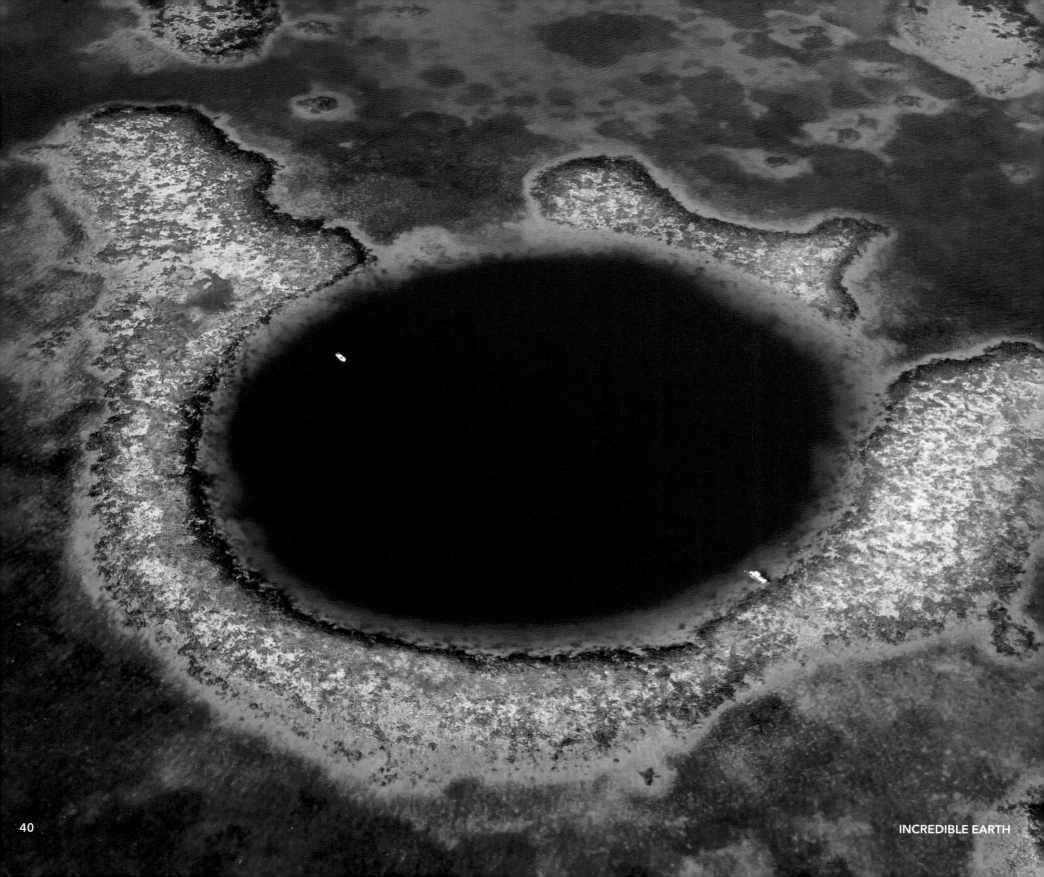

BLUE HOLES

Blue holes are gigantic sink holes on the ocean floor. They occur in parts of shallow, tropical seas where the underlying bedrock is made of limestone or coral.

They are so-named because of the contrast of the dark blue, deep waters of their depths to the lighter blue shallows which surround them. The difference in colour is particularly apparent when viewed from above.

The world's deepest blue hole is the Dragon Hole in the South China Sea at 300 m depth. Other famous blue holes occur in the Bahamas, Belize and the Turks and Caicos Islands, all in the western Atlantic. Due to their great depths and hazardous nature, only experienced cave divers are permitted to explore blue holes.

INCREDIBLE EARTH

GIANT CAVES

Caves are underground cavities that usually form as a result of weathering of rock, often by water-based erosive processes such as underground rivers.

Caves can occur within most rocks, but they are particularly common in sedimentary geology, and especially so in karst areas (comprised of limestone and related rock types).

The formation of caves may span vast amounts of geological time, sometimes continuing over millions of years, and many of the features inside caves may also take millenia to develop (e.g. stalactites and stalagmite, see page 47).

Although thousands of caves have been discovered, most speleologists believe that the majority of the world's caves remain to be found. Some authorities even claim that less than 1% of all caves have been discovered so far.

This is partly because most caves do not have an entrance. The majority are sealed underground voids, which are very difficult to locate from the surface.

The following are among the largest caves discovered so far. Look for the yellow circles, which show people for scale!

The world's largest natural cave is the Son Doong Cave, in Phong Nha-Ke Bang National Park in Vietnam.

A local man called Ho Khanh found the entrance to this cave in 1991, after he heard wind whistling and the roar of a rushing stream underground.

Son Doong Cave has since been extensively explored, and the main passage is now known to be over 5 km long, up to 200 m high and 150 m wide. This is so massive that a Boeing 747 could fly through the cave with considerable room to spare!

Another enormous cave-like gorge was discovered in southern Venezuela by explorer Charles Brewer-Carias in 2002. Named the Cave of the Ghosts in Spanish, its entrance is so enormous that two helicopters landed inside (see red circle on page 45).

STALACTITES AND STALAGMITES

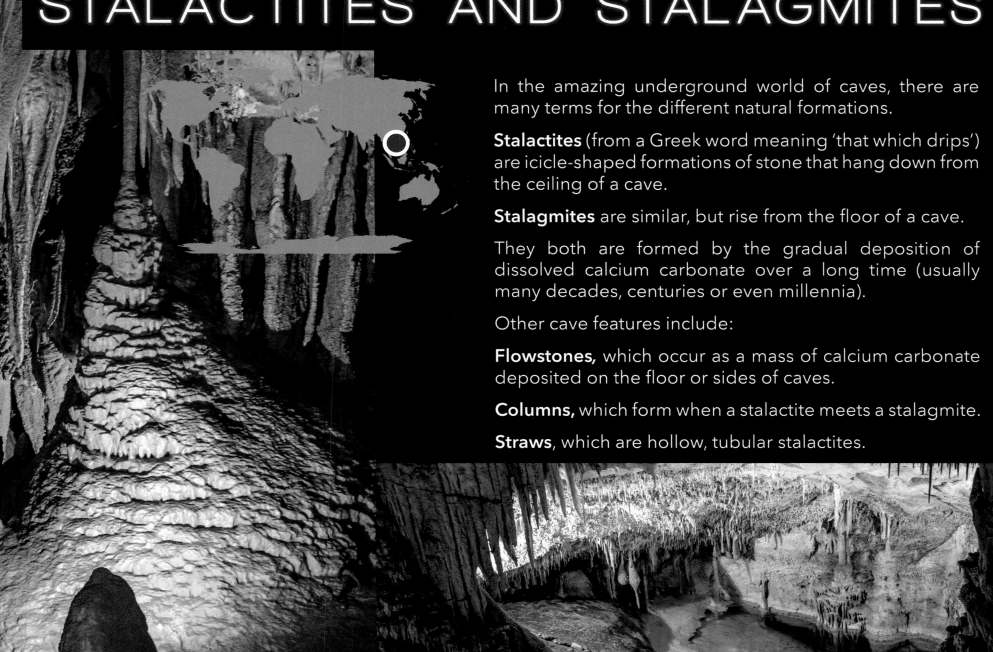

In the amazing underground world of caves, there are many terms for the different natural formations.

Stalactites (from a Greek word meaning 'that which drips') are icicle-shaped formations of stone that hang down from the ceiling of a cave.

Stalagmites are similar, but rise from the floor of a cave.

They both are formed by the gradual deposition of dissolved calcium carbonate over a long time (usually many decades, centuries or even millennia).

Other cave features include:

Flowstones, which occur as a mass of calcium carbonate deposited on the floor or sides of caves.

Columns, which form when a stalactite meets a stalagmite.

Straws, which are hollow, tubular stalactites.

The world's largest known stalagmite is in Son Doong Cave in Vietnam, and it's over 70 m in height!

Elsewhere in the world, artisans have carved cave formations into sculptures. For example, in the Shapur Cave, in the Zagros Mountains of south Iran, there stands a 3rd-century statue of Shapur I, second ruler of the Sassanid Empire. The statue was carved from a single stalagmite, and is nearly 7 m high.

CRYSTAL CAVES

In Chihuahua State, Mexico, lead, silver and zinc have been extracted at the Naica Mine for decades.

In 1975, some of the mine's flooded underground passages were drained so that they could be explored for minerals.

In the year 2000, two brothers and miners Juan and Pedro Sanchez explored the drained passages and discovered a 300 m long chamber filled with enormous gypsum crystals that are among the largest natural crystals ever found.

The very biggest crystals in the Naica Crystal Caves are over 1.2 m in diameter and 15 m long. A second chamber named the Cave of Swords is lined with lots of 1 m long gypsum crystals.

The gigantic crystals of the Naica Mine formed around 290 m below the surface of the ground.

Geothermal mineral-rich waters were driven up from the deeper passages within the mine. The liquid cooled within the Crystal Cave, and precipitated out the gypsum over hundreds of years. When the mine was drained in 1975, the crystals were exposed to air and stopped growing.

The geothermal heat within the mine makes exploration difficult. The temperature can exceed 55°C, and there is so little oxygen that specialised suits with oxygen tanks are needed for visits longer than 10 minutes.

In 2008, a worker at the mine tried to enter the Crystal Cave to steal some of the gypsum, but he became lost and suffocated in the cave's inhospitable atmosphere.

The Naica Mine has declared that once all research on the giant crystals has been completed, the Crystal Cave will be flooded again, to enable the crystals to continue growing and to protect them for the future.

GLOWWORM CAVES

The Waitomo Caves on the North Island of New Zealand are a series of connected limestone chambers with a rather peculiar natural lightshow.

The caves were first explored during the 1880s, and the first visitors noticed that the cave ceiling and walls were covered with thousands of pin-pricks of cool, bluish light.

Each glow was surrounded by a curtain of transparent beaded threads hanging down from the ceiling.

The explorers wondered what was the cause of the strange lights in the dark cave chambers.

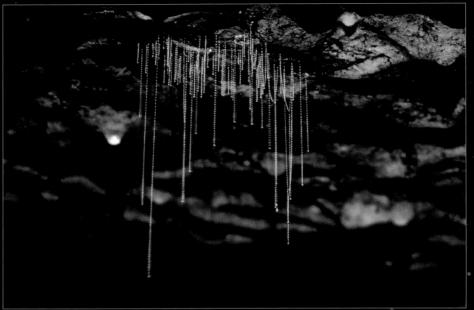

It turned out the glowing points within the Waitomo Caves are caused by the larvae of the fungus gnat *Arachnocampa luminosa*, commonly known as the New Zealand glowworm.

The larvae are worm-like and produce a blue-green bioluminescent glow from the moment they hatch from their eggs.

When they are 3-4 cm long, they produce up to 30 silk threads lined with small sticky droplets, which they hang from the cave ceilings or walls.

Each larva then waits in the middle of its threads, hoping that insects will fly into the cave. Many flying insects are attracted to the lights (like moths to a flame). Once inside the cave, insects see the points of light and interpret them to be a way out, and so fly towards them and become tangled in the curtain of sticky threads.

Once their prey is caught, the thread is pulled up by the larva through ingestion, eventually devouring the trapped tasty morsel of prey.

The glowworm's bioluminescence is produced from its abdomen, by means of a luciferin-luciferase reaction (see page 36).

Scientists have found that the light emitted from a hungry glowworm is stronger than that produced from one that has just eaten.

Once the glowworm has undergone four moults (gradually growing larger each time), it pupates for two weeks before hatching out as an adult gnat.

The adults cannot feed: their sole purpose is to find a mate and for the female to lay eggs. But during this search, they have to make sure they avoid all the sticky threads around them!

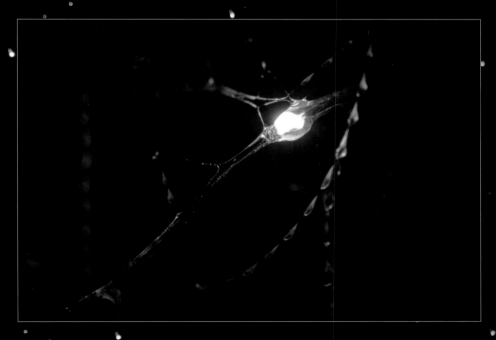

GLOWWORM CAVES

DESERTS AND OASES

Deserts are extremely dry environments that receive a maximum of around 250 mm of rainfall a year. They cover about one fifth of the Earth's surface.

Deserts are found on every continent, and include some of the world's last areas of true wilderness.

Although deserts are often thought of as extremely hot places, not all of them are. Some of the world's most arid landscapes occur close to the poles (see page 97).

The largest hot desert is the Sahara in northern Africa. Hot deserts are often characterised by sand, which may be blown into massive dune systems that cover thousands of square kilometres.

Although deserts are extreme environments, they do harbour many plants and animals that are specially-adapted to arid conditions.

The most famous desert-dweller is perhaps the camel, which stores food and water in distinctive fatty deposits known as "humps" on its back.

There are three species of camel across the world: the common one-humped dromedary camel, and the rare domestic Bactrian camel (shown here) and the wild Bactrian camel, both of which have two humps.

Due to the reserves in their humps, during the hottest times of the year, camels can survive for up to a week without drinking. During winter, they may survive for over six months without a drink, and can survive by obtaining moisture from the plants they consume.

Desert chameleons (below) can also survive drought, for they have impermeable skin that reduces water loss!

Living in deserts presents many challenges. Desert geckos (left) have special feet with broad toes that allow them to grip the sand without sinking in. This adaptation enables them to run really fast over sand dunes!

Desert beetles can even collect moisture from the air!

One species that lives in the deserts of Namibia has special grooves and bumps on its body (shown here). During cool nights,the beetle faces into the breeze and raises its back, which allows droplets of moisture to condense from fog. The droplets then roll down the beetles back to its mouth.

Many animals survive in deserts by having light body colours that reflect heat, such as the oryx (below).

Plants can also survive in extremely dry deserts. The quiver tree of southern Africa has white bark that reflects heat. It has succulent leaves that loose little water, and a swollen stem filled with spongy tissues that store water! In extreme drought, it can even shed its foliage to reduce water consumption.

For thousands of years, civilisations have existed in many of the most extreme deserts on Earth, often close to oases.

An oasis is a pocket of fertile wetlands in a desert, usually fed by an underground water reserve (such as an aquifer), a river or a lake. Above is the Huacachina oasis in Peru.

Oases may form islands of green in an otherwise barren landscape. They are a haven for wildlife and farmers!

Over the centuries, many desert-dwelling peoples have built complex cities and highly developed civilisations.

The Great Mosque of Djenné in Mali (below) was constructed in 1907. The walls are made from sun-baked mud bricks coated with a muddy plaster, giving the facade a smooth look. It is the largest building made of mud in the world, and since 1988, has been listed as a World Heritage Site.

Due to their lack of clouds, deserts are famed around the world for having some of the clearest night skies which offer some of the most beautiful starscapes visible on Earth.

The lack of insulative clouds can also make desert nights extremely cold. The temperature difference in some deserts between day and night can exceed 40°C.

Some extreme deserts may receive virtually no precipitation at all for years on end. When it does rain, water may flow over the baked ground and form rivers that drain quickly away.

Bizarrely, flash floods can occur in deserts where there has been no rain, as water can flow in the dry river beds from rainy areas many kilometres away.

Wet areas in deserts can suddenly dry out, killing the vegetation, as occurred at Deadvlei, Namibia (shown below).

64

GEYSERS AND FUMAROLES

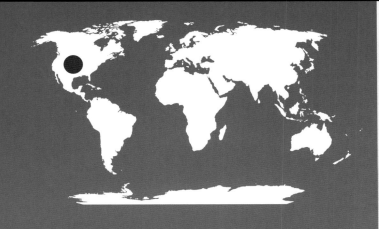

Geysers and fumaroles occur when water is heated to high temperatures deep within the Earth's crust, causing it to boil and erupt to the surface.

Geysers intermittently spout jets of hot water and steam into the air. They usually erupt at regular intervals, as the pressure takes a predictable amount of time to build up.

Fumaroles release superheated water vapour, often continually and without interruption.

Both geysers and fumeroles may release other gases as well, such as carbon dioxide, sulphur dioxide and hydrogen chloride.

The release of volcanic gases, as well as minerals dissolved in water, often causes colourful encrustations to develop around active geyser and fumarole vents.

Geysers and fumaroles occur in hydrothermal areas around the world, which are often associated with volcanic activity.

The greatest concentrations of geysers and fumaroles occur in the Yellowstone National Park, USA.

Yellowstone has over 500 active geysers, including the world's tallest predictable geyser, known as the 'Grand Geyser', which blasts water to a height of 61 m for up to 10 minutes every 7-15 hours.

The park is also home to around 4,000 active fumaroles!

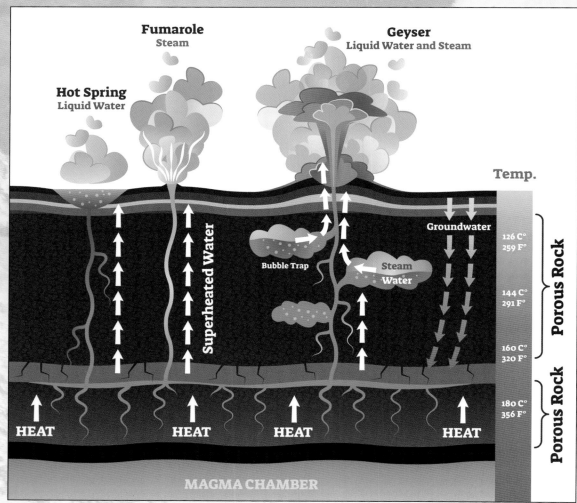

GEYSERS AND FUMAROLES

HOT SPRINGS

Hot springs are sources of geothermally-heated groundwater. They often form pools that may be lined with exquisite encrustations of colourful minerals that are precipitated out as the water evaporates.

The water of hot springs varies in temperature, but may be close to boiling point! Many sulphurous gases are often released as the water emerges, and this often gives a strong aroma of rotten eggs to these areas.

Grand Prismatic Spring (shown here) is the third largest hot spring in the world. Located within the Yellowstone National Park, it is also one of the most colourful, not only because of minerals, but also because of microbial mats that form around the edges of its waters. The colours change during the year, with reds and oranges in summer, giving way to dark greens in winter.

For thousands of years, many hot springs have attracted tourists. Springs with waters that have a temperature range conducive to human bathing have long been regarded as having therapeutic benefits.

The town of Bath in England owes its existence (and name) to hot springs! The springs were first discovered by Prince Bladud around 863 BC, and were developed by the Romans for their relaxation.

BUBBLING MUD

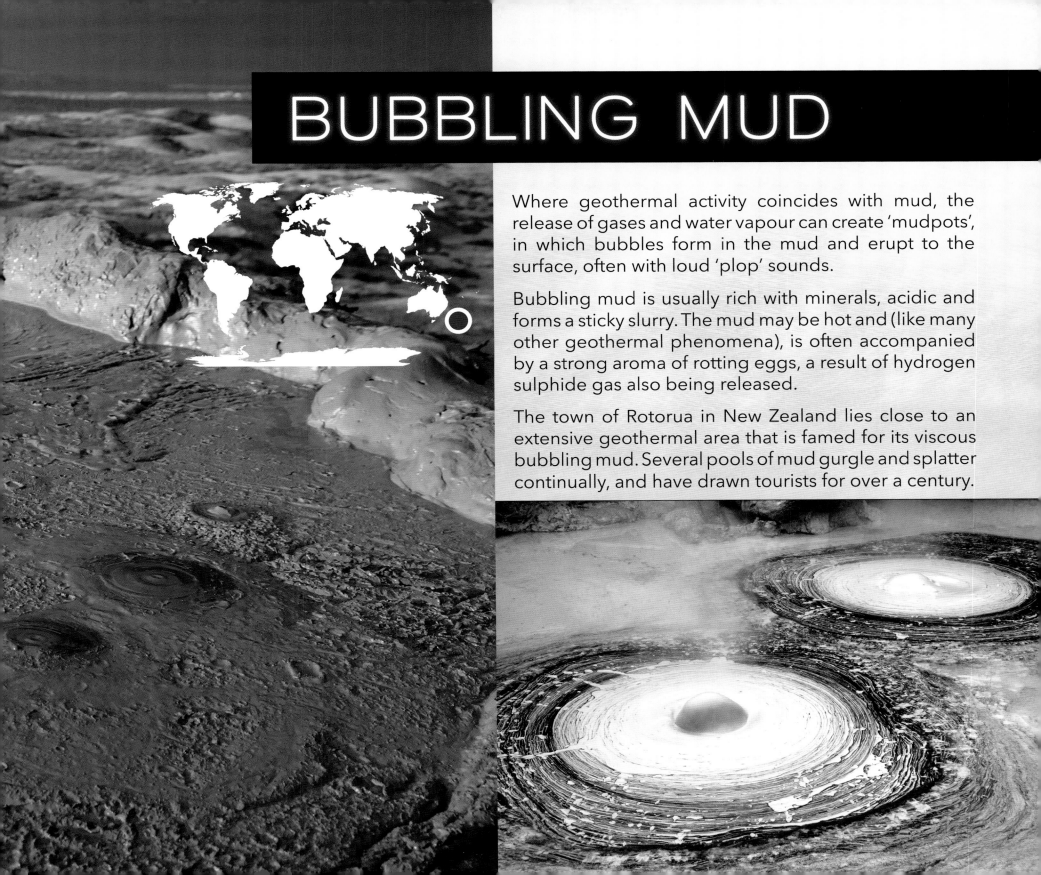

Where geothermal activity coincides with mud, the release of gases and water vapour can create 'mudpots', in which bubbles form in the mud and erupt to the surface, often with loud 'plop' sounds.

Bubbling mud is usually rich with minerals, acidic and forms a sticky slurry. The mud may be hot and (like many other geothermal phenomena), is often accompanied by a strong aroma of rotting eggs, a result of hydrogen sulphide gas also being released.

The town of Rotorua in New Zealand lies close to an extensive geothermal area that is famed for its viscous bubbling mud. Several pools of mud gurgle and splatter continually, and have drawn tourists for over a century.

The bubbling mud of many mudpots around the world has long been believed to hold healing properties. At El Totumo in Columbia, visitors completely immerse themselves in the warm, gloopy mud for apparent skin healing benefits! Would you fancy a dip?

Mudpots are very different to mud volcanoes, which arise when mud and water are mixed below ground under pressure, then forced through cracks in the crust to form cone-shaped accumulations around active vents (see photos on page 77).

While mudpots are usually limited in size, the cones of mud volcanoes can grow to over 700 m high and 10 km wide (such as the world's largest mud volcano, the Sidoarjo Mudflow, in Lusi, Indonesia).

Azerbaijan has the greatest concentrations of mud volcanoes, with over 400 scattered around the country (around half of all mud volcanoes known worldwide).

One interpretation of the name 'Azerbaijan' refers to its reputation as 'the land of fire'. This may be because several mud volcanoes occur across Azerbaijan that continually release methane, which burns with bright orange flames!

In 2001, a large mud volcano located 15 km from Baku (the country's capital), made headlines around the world when it blasted out a jet of burning gas 15 m into the air!

GIANT WATERFALLS

The great rivers of the world are home to many gigantic cataracts (or large waterfalls). Each differs in height, width, water volume and flow speed, but they include some of the most dramatic natural spectacles on the planet.

The 82 m high Iguazú Falls (shown here) are found on the border between Argentina and Brazil in South America.

They are the world's largest series of waterfalls by volume. Thousands of tonnes of water thunder down the cascades of the Iguazú Falls every minute.

During the dry season, water flows over several hundred individual falls, but after heavy rain, most of the cascades combine into just a few immense curtains of flowing water.

The tallest waterfall in the world is Venezuela's Angel Falls (shown on the left here) which plunges 979 m over the side of Auyan Tepui (one of the 'lost world' plateaus, see page 103).

Angel Falls is named after an American explorer and bush pilot, Jimmy Angel, who spotted the waterfall from the window of his plane in 1933.

A few years later, Jimmy deliberately crash landed on the summit of Auyán Tepui to search for gold not far from the top of Angel Falls, although unfortunately he did not find any, and had to climb down the mountain side, leaving his plane behind.

The volume of water flowing over Angel Falls is minuscule compared to the Iguazú Falls, but the fact that it is over ten times as high means that the stream of water can take more than a minute to reach the bottom! Much of the water that flows over Angel Falls turns to spray by the time is touches the ground.

Other impressive falls include:

Skogafoss Fall on Iceland, which has a 60 m tall cascade (page 81, top left).

Victoria Falls: located on the border of Zimbabwe with Zambia, which have a fall of 108 m (page 81, top right).

Niagara Falls: on the border of Canada with the USA, with a fall of 51 m (page 81, bottom).

The 'spray zone' around many large waterfalls gives rise to unique habitats that support specialised plants, amphibians and invertebrates. Some of these species occur at a single waterfall and nowhere else on Earth!

INCREDIBLE EARTH

FROZEN LAKES

The central regions of continents often experience extremely cold winter temperatures, and during the coldest months, lakes in these areas undergo a serious deep freeze.

Lake Baikal is one of the clearest examples. It is located in Siberia, Russia, and is the world's largest body of freshwater by volume. It contains more water than the North American Great Lakes combined.

The lake is rich in biodiversity, and hosts many endemic species that are very unusual in lake ecosystems, including the world's only population of freshwater seals, and several species of freshwater sponges.

In wintertime, the surface of Lake Baikal freezes over for up to 5 months. In places, the ice can be over 2 m thick.

The ice actually protects the lake ecosystem from the extreme cold of the Siberian winter.

Although the air temperature may regularly fall below -30°C, the water temperature actually increases with depth away from the frozen surface, reaching 3.5°C at around 250 m.

As the water is particularly well oxygenated, fish and other aquatic life survive through winter, unhindered by the ice sheets that cover the surface.

Large bubbles of methane gas are continually released from rotting organic material on the bed of the lake.

During winter, the bubbles of methane become trapped under the ice, then frozen into layers as the ice thickens.

The bubbles of methane are highly flammable, and burst into flame if punctured and ignited.

With the coming of spring, a gradual thaw sets in and the winter ice begins to break up.

Strong winds are not unusual, and often result in waves on the lake up to 4.5 m high. The winds may also whip up surface spray which can then re-freeze on any object it lands on around the lake shores.

This phenomenon of freezing spray can occur around lakes throughout temperate regions of the world, and in extreme cases, cars may be covered (shown here) and entire buildings have been known to collapse with the additional weight of tonnes of ice upon them.

As the surface ice of temperate lakes breaks into pieces, strong winds may drive it into piles at the lake's edges, causing the shattered pieces to accumulate on top of one another like sheets of glass before melting.

GLACIERS AND ICEBERGS

Glaciers are accumulations of snow and ice, that become compressed as dense ice masses. Despite being frozen, they move slowly and flow downhill, driven by their own immense weight.

Moving glaciers are the most powerful erosive force on land. A glacier may exert thousands of tonnes of weight on the ground and will scour the substrate or underlying bedrock as it flows.

The lower surface of a glacier may melt from pressure or friction, then periodically refreeze, gripping rocks the size of houses, and dragging them along its path. The debris the glacier carries can scratch and scrap the surfaces it travels over, pulverising solid rock.

Most of the world's glaciers occur on Antarctica and Greenland, but a few are found in mountains across the world, including ones in the tropics (e.g. Mount Kilimanjaro).

When a glacier reaches the sea, it usually breaks into pieces as the differing density of the water causes the front end to flex. This process is known as 'calving', and the lumps of ice that break off become icebergs.

Since icebergs consist of frozen fresh water, they float in seawater because the salt content of sea water makes it around 10% heavier than fresh water. As such, 90% of an iceberg's volume (and mass) is hidden under the waves. Picture the iceberg below and imagine nice times more ice below the sea!

Icebergs can range in size from just a few cubic meters (known as 'growlers' or 'bergy bits') right up to the size of small countries!

In 2019, a giant iceberg broke away from the Ross Ice Shelf in Antarctica. It was named D-28, and measured as having an area of 1,636 km^2 (twice the size of New York City), and with an estimated weight over 315 billion tonnes. Such enormous icebergs may persist for years before melting.

Serious suggestions have been made by countries in the Middle East that giant icebergs could be towed from Antarctica to the Persian Gulf, to provide sources of freshwater (as even in tropical heat, the giant masses of ice may take weeks or months to melt.

Sometimes, a hole may develop through a melting iceberg. This may expand until it forms an ice arch before collapsing. Ice arches over 30 m wide are not uncommon!

10%

90%

Icebergs provide an essential habitat for many marine animals, including polar bears, seals and penguins.

Polar bears use ice floes as their favourite hunting grounds, whereas seals and penguins use 'tabular' icebergs (which have flat tops) as resting places and look-out posts.

While most icebergs are made of white glacial ice, some may contain streaks of refrozen meltwater that is often bright blue! Others have inclusions of gravel or glacial debris, and so can have black or brown stripes!

Sometimes, large quantities of meltwater refreezes within glacial crevasses. If calved, this can form entire icebergs that are bright blue or transparent like glass.

The rarest icebergs are bright green, resulting from algae or phytoplankton becoming frozen within the ice.

As icebergs melt, their shape alters, therefore changing the iceberg's centre of gravity. As this happens, a berg may suddenly roll over, often breaking apart as it moves. This can make icebergs very dangerous to approach.

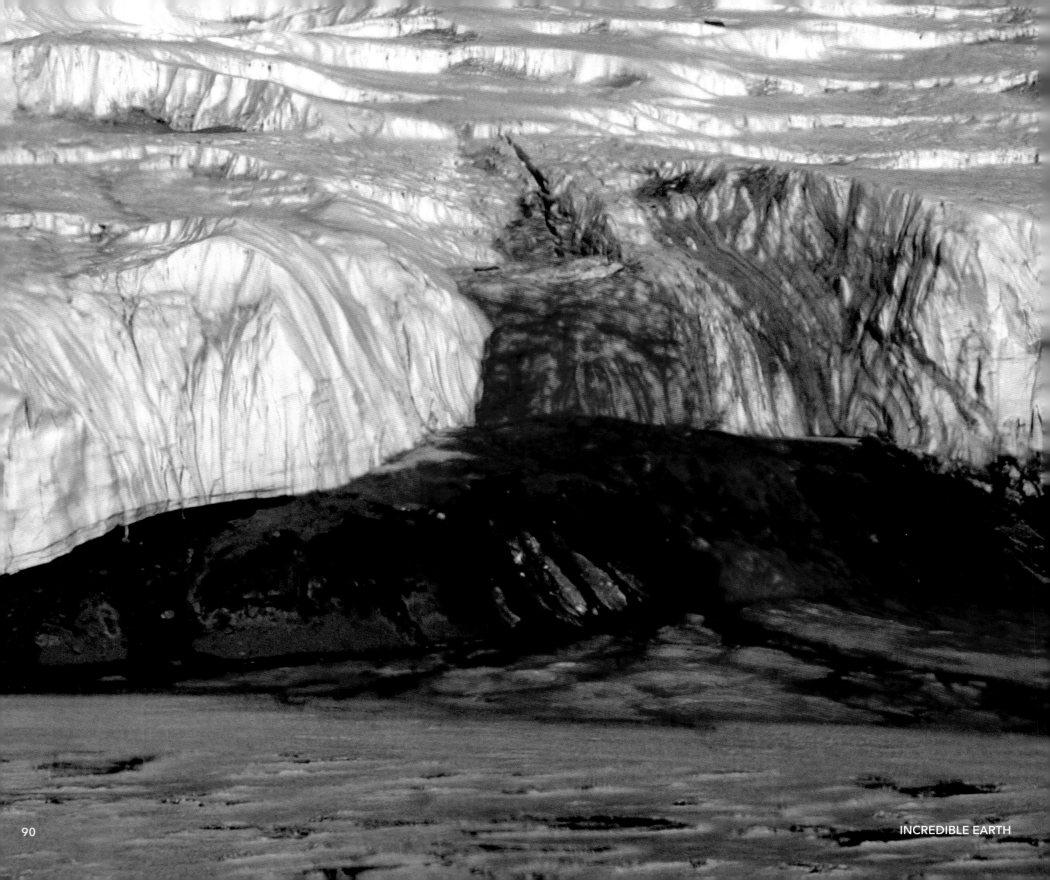

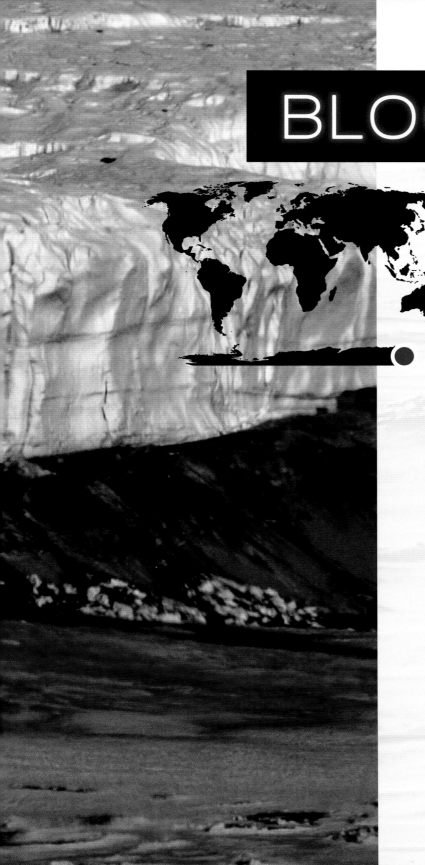

BLOOD FALLS

Blood Falls is an unusual waterfall that flows out from small fissures in the ice of Taylor Glacier, located in the Taylor Valley, in the east of Antarctica.

The falls is unusual because the liquid that emerges is bright red and resembles blood!

Blood Falls was first sighted in 1911 by the Australian geologist Griffith Taylor, who first explored the valley that bears his name.

Most of the early Antarctic explorers who saw Blood Falls attributed the red colour of the 'blood liquid' to red algae, but it was later proven that the reddish colour results from iron oxides.

The red liquid of Blood Falls is salty, and it is believed to flow from a sub-glacial pool that lies underneath the ice many kilometres way. It has been speculated that the pool may be 400 m deep below the ice.

If these theories are correct, a river of 'blood' flows underneath the Taylor Glacier like a blood vessel!

Glaciologists believe many lakes may occur underneath the ice of Antarctica, and it has been suggested that some of them may even contain microscopic life that has been isolated from the rest of the world for thousands of years!

Although this does not seem to be the case for Blood Falls, this strange waterfall raises the question as to what else might lie underneath the ice of Antarctica?

INCREDIBLE EARTH

ICE SHEETS AND ICE CAVES

By definition, an ice sheet is a mass of glacial ice that covers an area greater than 50,000 km².

Currently, there are only two ice sheets on Earth, although during past times of colder climates (such as the ice ages), many other ice sheets have existed, mainly covering upland areas around the world.

Of the two currently existing ice sheets, the Antarctica ice sheet covers an area of over 14 million km². It contains about 61% of all the freshwater on Earth, and if it were to completely melt, global sea levels would rise by at least 58 m!

The other existing ice sheet is the Greenland ice sheet, which covers over 1.7 million km², and contains sufficient freshwater to rise sea levels by around 7 m.

The ice which makes up the Antarctic and Greenland ice sheets is immensely old.

It is possible to date ice sheets because the ice forms distinct annual layers as it is deposited (just like the growth rings in the wood of a tree).

By counting how many layers deep an ice sheet is, glaciologists can establish precisely how many years ago the ice was first laid down. The thickest deposits of ice on Earth occur in Antarctica, where the ice sheet can be over 4,800 m deep! Ice at this depth is over 6 million years old!

Glaciologists drill through the ice to extract samples and to analyse bubbles of air trapped in the ice, revealing important information about the past climate.

Even though ice sheets are enormous and frozen, they are not static. Sections of ice sheets slowly flow towards low lying areas, similar to the movement of glaciers.

As the ice moves, meltwater channels within the ice, hollow out vast ice chasms and chambers. These ice caves can be dangerous to explore because the ice is often unstable, especially during summertime.

Despite the risks, glaciologists and climatologists venture into ice caves to collect important samples of ice. They use metal spikes on their boots (called crampons) which enable them to grip the ice, and specially designed ice axes to provide a firm hold for their hands.

Depending upon the depth of an ice cave, sunlight may shine through the ice cave's walls, and icicles can form inside the cave like stalactites and stalagmites!

DRY VALLEYS

Most people associate the word 'desert' with images of the Sahara, camels and sand dunes. But many of the most arid landscapes on Earth occur at polar latitudes and are extremely cold.

The covering of ice over the poles reduces the amount of evaporation, and powerful katabatic winds prevent rainfall from occurring. As such, Antarctica is the driest continent on Earth.

The Dry Valleys of Antarctica (and their equivalent near to the North Pole) receive less than 100 mm of precipitation a year. All of this falls in the form of snow, which evaporates in the dry air within minutes, leaving the ground bone dry.

Unsurprisingly, very little life can survive within polar dry valleys. In some coastal areas, algae may grow within sandstone rocks between the grains of sand. But in more exposed areas, not even bacteria and fungi may survive.

Animals such as seals or penguins sometimes become lost in Antarctica's dry valleys and die. Their bodies are freeze-dried, and may stay preserved for thousands of years in the sterile conditions a bit like Egyptian mummies!

Scientists have dated some of the preserved animal bodies to be over 20,000 years old, yet they look virtually unchanged since the day the animal died.

Antarctica's Dry Valleys are not only extremely cold and dry, but they are also among the windiest places on Earth! Wind speeds at over 150 km/per hour have been recorded!

These incredibly powerful winds are so strong that they blow sand particles and carve rocks! These so-called 'ventifacts' (wind carved rocks) often have strange, smooth shapes and forms.

All of these extreme conditions make Antarctica's Dry Valleys among the most inhospitable places on Earth.

The British Antarctic explorers Captain Robert Falcon Scott and Sir Ernest Henry Shackleton set up their expedition huts not far from the Dry Valleys.

Although conditions are not quite as extreme at the huts compared to the Dry Valleys, the aridity and low temperatures of the Antarctic climate have perfectly preserved the contents of the explorers' bases.

The food, clothing and beds that the explorers left remain unchanged. Even the bodies of sledge dogs are preserved outside the huts, just like the unfortunate freeze-dried seals and penguins in the Dry Valleys nearby.

JASPER CREEK

In the south of Venezuela, there flows a small waterfall unlike any other. The water tumbles over a bedrock of blood-red jasper, a semi-precious gemstone used around the world to make jewelry!

The gigantic slab of jasper is over 100 m long, and black algae grow in groves along its surface, making a 'tiger skin' pattern.

The Jasper Creek is strictly protected, since the value of all that gemstone is incalculable!

Since jasper is translucent, the colour of the bedrock can appear to differ, depending upon the amount of sunlight falling upon it. On a really sunny day, the creek can seem to almost glow bright red!

INCREDIBLE EARTH

LOST WORLDS

Across the north of South American, over 100 gigantic sandstone plateaus rise above the clouds.

Known as 'tepuis' (or 'tepuyes'), these huge plateaus have vertical cliffs up to 1,000 m tall, and (in some cases) completely flat summits.

They are known as 'lost worlds' because, to varying degrees, they have been isolated from the rest of the world for millions of years, and harbour animals, plants and landscapes that occur nowhere else on Earth. Victorian naturalists seriously believed they could be home to prehistoric life or even to ancient civilizations.

After the tepuis were first sighted in the 16th century, it took explorers over 250 years to reach their summits!

During the 19th century, waves of explorers failed to reach the tops of the tepuis, and claimed that only by building a gigantic scaffold, or using a hot air balloon or a 'winged Pegasus' would the summits ever be reached.

The *Spectator* newspaper called the lost worlds "the greatest marvel and mystery of the Earth", but eventually, the summits of the tepuis were declared "forever beyond the reach of mankind".

Just when all hope had been abandoned, a ledge was sighted up the slopes of Mount Roraima (page 102).

A party of intrepid British explorers set out and, after a difficult journey, they finally climbed to the top of Mount Roraima, and discovered a 'lost world' that had never been seen before.

The view on top of Mount Roraima defies belief. Those first explorers described it as a "some strange country of nightmares", for it is a landscape of twisted stones, towers and arches carved by the wind and rain.

Labyrinthine rock spires as tall as a house stretch for kilometres, and in some areas, the ground is covered with sparkling quartz crystals.

Much of the wildlife of the lost world evolved there over millions of years, and occurs nowhere else on Earth. There are many plants that catch insects, including

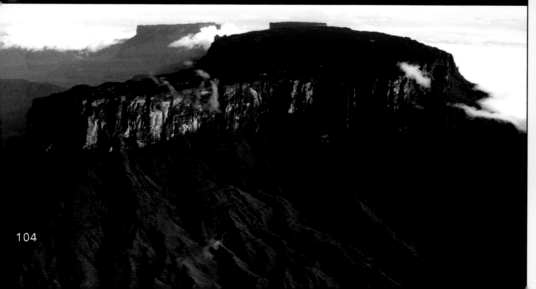

sundews that have leaves lined with glue, and colourful pitcher plants with hollow leaves (page 104).

Some of the plants of the lost worlds have iridescent blue leaves (bottom right), while animal life includes black pebble toads, poisonous yellow and black dart frogs, oil birds with a form of echolocation, and horned spiders with spikes on their abdomens!

Even though the explorers didn't find any dinosaurs, the story of the exploration of Mount Roraima inspired Sir Arthur Conan Doyle (the author of the Sherlock Holmes books) to write a fictional story called *The Lost World*, and, more recently, the Pixar/Disney film *UP*.

METEORITE CRATERS

Around 44 tonnes of space rocks (called 'meteoroids') enter the atmosphere every day. They vary in size and pass through the atmosphere at speeds of over 72,000 km/hr.

Most small meteoroids (meteors) burn up as a result of the extremely high temperatures created by friction with the atmosphere. This process produces a streak of bright light, which we commonly refer to as a "shooting star".

Larger meteoroids may be big enough to survive entering the atmosphere, and will crash down on the surface of Earth, often leaving a crater. These are called meteorites.

One of the best examples of a meteorite crater occurs in the desert near Flagstaff, Arizona, USA. The crater is 1.2 km across and 170 m deep, and results from an impact event that happened about 50,000 years ago!

INCREDIBLE EARTH

MINERAL TERRACES

In many parts of the world, evaporation causes streams of freshwaters to deposit encrustations of minerals, which form exquisite terraces and pools.

The sources of these mineral-rich waters may be geothermal springs or geysers, but not always. They can form from the water of slow-moving streams that flow through mineral rich rocks.

Depending upon the minerals in the freshwater, the terraces may consist of calcium-based substances, such as travertine, and may grow extremely slowly over many millennia.

Two of the world's best systems of Mineral terraces are at Pamukkale in Turkey (shown here), which consist of dazzling white terraces, and Huanglong in China (pages 110-111), which consist of yellowish minerals.

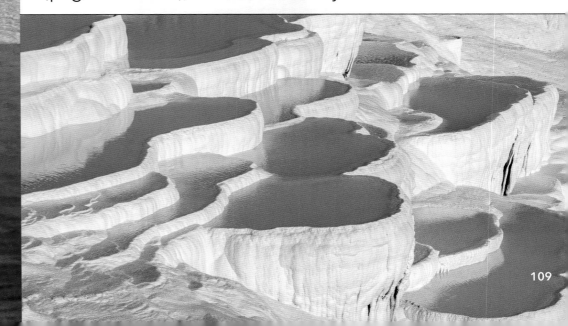

The mineral terraces of Huanglong, China (shown here), have developed over several kilometres as spring water flows down a mountain side.

The terraces vary in colour, but are mostly made of yellowish minerals, and the waters contained within the terrace pools are bright blue!

Diverse groves of wildflowers grow around the pools, and even into the water. Some of the species have adapted to the chemical composition of the sulphur-rich waters.

Many species of orchids grow along the banks of the pools, including two species of slipper orchids (*Cypripedium*) with purple and yellow flowers respectively (shown on page 111).

MOERAKI BOULDERS

The Moeraki bounders are large, spheres of rock on a stretch of Koekohe beach on the Otago coast of the south island of New Zealand. They are unusual because of their size and almost perfect spherical shape.

Most of the Moeraki boulders are 1.5 - 2.2 m in diameter and they were once enclosed within mudstone that constitutes the cliff at the back of the beach. Detailed analysis of the boulders has revealed that they are made of mud, fine silt and clay cemented together by calcite, and they have hollow centres.

It is believed they were formed during the Palaeocene epoch, between 66 - 56 million years ago.

AMERICAN BADLANDS

The arid, eroded 'badlands' of the American south-west are home to some of the most spectacular landscapes in the New World.

Monument Valley, on the Arizona-Utah border, is among the region's most famous landscapes, being used as a backdrop in countless western (cowboy) movies.

It forms part of the Colorado Plateau and is characterised by a cluster of large sandstone buttes. The tallest of these reaches a height of 300 m above the valley floor.

The red colour of the buttes derives from exposed iron oxide within the siltstone rock.

The erosive actions of wind and water over the past 50 million years have weathered the land, leaving behind these majestic formations.

Near to Monument Valley, the Colorado River snakes its way through the arid landscape, often with dramatic bends along its course, including Horseshoe Bend (shown to the left).

Downstream, the Grand Canyon has also been formed by the Colorado River. At its deepest point, the canyon bottom lies over 1.8 km below nearby sections of the canyon's rim.

This region harboured many tribes of native Pueblo peoples, some of which built cliffside dwellings and storage granaries that were hidden from their enemies and could be protected from attack.

The most spectacular Puebloan settlement was built at Mesa Verde. Known as the Cliff Palace, it consists of a series of stone buildings constructed on a ledge around 800 years ago (page 117).

The American south-west is home to a mysterious phenomenon that baffled geologists for many years.

Rocks on valley floors often have long tracks in the ground behind them, showing that they have moved but without any human or animal intervention. They came to be known as 'sliding rocks' or 'walking stones'.

After much study, geologists discovered that the valleys flood during winter, and the surface of the water freezes around any loose rock and grips it.

If the sheet of ice is then blown by the wind, the rock is moved along the valley floor. When the temperature rises, all traces of the ice that carried the rock disappears.

INCREDIBLE EARTH

PINNACLES

The thousands of different rock types that occur across our planet all erode in different ways.

Many sedimentary rocks are susceptible to the action of rain water, or carbonic acid dissolved within rain water, and under certain conditions, these rocks may erode into spectacular landscapes of pinnacles.

Many processes can cause pinnacles to form. One of the most common arises when layers of harder rock occur over softer strata. As the hard rock erodes, sections may remain and prevent erosion taking place directly beneath them. Water then washes away the softer sediments between the remaining hard sections, slowly carving out pinnacles beneath the more resistant sections.

This process has led to the sandstone pinnacles at the Bryce Canyon National Park, Utah (shown here), and similar ones in northern Madagascar (page 120).

In many parts of the world, the (weak) acidic action of rainwater can also form pinnacles, especially in areas of karst rock, such as limestone.

Over thousands of years, acid accumulates in cracks in the limestone and gradually dissolves grooves in the surface of the rock.

The grooves collect more rainwater and more acid, and over time, the erosion is concentrated and eats downwards into the rock. Gradually, blade-like pinnacles emerge and the rock is eroded away.

Two examples of pinnacles that formed through this process are those of Mount Api in Malaysian Borneo (page 121, low left), which tower over 20 metres tall, and the vast landscapes of pinnacles of Ankarana in northern Madagascar, which cover an area of many km^2.

Limestone pinnacles are often razor sharp and brittle, so can be very dangerous to climbers.

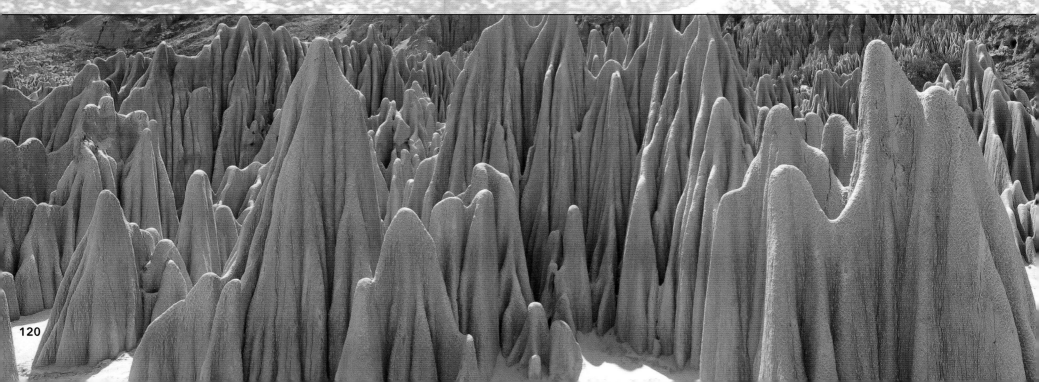

PINK LAKES

Bright pink lakes are known from many parts of the world, with some of the best examples occurring in Australia.

During the summer months, water evaporates from the shallow brine lakes, increasing their salinity to a point which most organisms cannot tolerate.

However, providing temperature and nutrient levels are right, two organisms may thrive in the saline conditions: a bacterium (*Halobacterium cutirubrum*) and an alga (*Dunaliella salina*). As their populations explode due to lack of competition and predators, the red carotenoid pigments secreted by these organisms turn the lake waters strawberry milkshake pink!

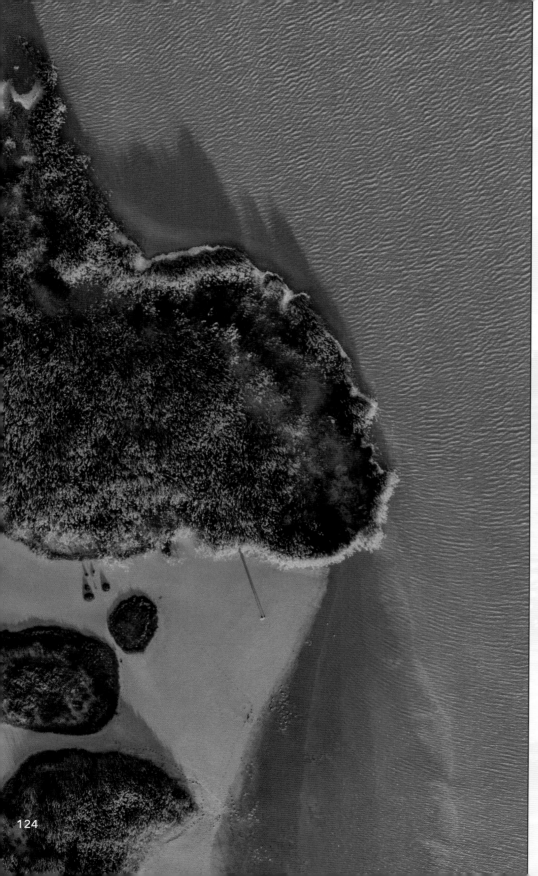

Once levels of rain increase and the salinity of the lake water falls again, the pink colour of the lake water usually disappears, as the ecosystem normalises.

The process of a lake turning pink can be very rapid, sometimes taking place within just a few days. However, a particular lake may not become pink every year. Some pink lakes turn pink only sporadically, when conditions are just right.

Lake Hillier in Western Australia and Lake Bumbunga in South Australia are among the lakes that most frequently turn pink, with the two lakes often displaying especially vivid pink waters.

Dunaliella salina, the alga partly responsible for the pink hue, is commercially farmed for its pink pigment (beta-carotene), which is used as a food additive and as a natural colourant.

As the water level of a pink lake decreases, salt will crystalise on objects remaining in the water, for example, the strange, giant pink mushrooms-like salt encrustations in the photo below. These have formed on sticks protruding out of the water surface.

At some lakes, pink salt crystals are harvested commercially. Pink salt is very valuable, and sought after by chefs for its cooking and preserving qualities, and because it apparently adds flavour to food.

RAINBOW MOUNTAINS

Sedimentary rocks differ in colour as a result of their mineral content or component material composition.

Many mountains across the world consist of multiple strata that differ in colour, but in a few extreme cases, lots of radically different rock types may be layered on top of one another to create rainbow mountains!

Some of the most colourful rainbow mountains occur at Vinicunca, in the Peruvian Andes. There, steeply tilted strata create stripes of seven distinct colours: pink, red, white, green, blue, brown and yellow.

The rainbow of colours are the result of differing bands of clay, mud, sand, quartz, sandstone and marl. In some areas, erosion of the strata has resulted in 'candy-cane' alternating stripes of red, white and pink!

The rainbow mountains of Vinicunca are located at an altitude of over 5,000 m. Herds of alpacas roam across the colourful slopes, munching on the few plants that they can find.

Although the alpacas are oblivious to the colourful scenery, they are encouraged by local tour operators to thin the vegetation and ensure the spectacular geological colours remain visible to attract tourists!

Spectacular rainbow mountains are also found in the Akzhar Mountains of the Karaganda region of Kazakhstan, and in the Zhangye National Geopark, in Gansu, China.

At these sites, multi-coloured layers of sandstones have been eroded into cliffs, ravines and pillars of varying hues and patterns.

SALT LANDSCAPES

In many parts of the world, salt pans have developed as a result of inland bodies of salty water evaporating, leaving behind layers of salt on the surface of the ground.

Few organisms can survive in pure salt, so most salt pans are uninterrupted, lifeless landscapes of reflective white salt crystals.

The layer of salt that makes up a salt pan can be tens of metres thick (such as the Danakil Depression, Ethiopia), which gives an indication of the size and depth of the body of salt water that existed before drying up.

In many salt pans, periodic flooding followed by evaporation results in the formation of large salt crystals and, often relatively regular polygonal geometric patterns across the surface of the salt (page 130).

Salt pans can be dangerous places. A surface crust of salt can conceal a quagmire of sticky salt-mud that can engulf vehicles, people or animals. The Qattara Depression in the Sahara Desert, was regarded as a deathtrap during World War II as it even trapped tanks!

But salt pans can also be lifelines.

Salt has been mined from salt pans across the world for thousands of years, and was an essential commodity for ancient civilisations.

Blocks of salt have been hacked out of the vast salt pans of Ethiopia's Danakil Depression since at least the 6th century, and continue to be mined today. The resulting blocks, known as 'amole', were traded for centuries across the Sahara, even to Europe and the Middle East!

The Afar people of the Danakil Depression continue to mine and trade amole blocks, and still use camel caravans to transport the precious cargo.

Many salt pans flood each year, and as the water evaporates, the brine crystalises in the form of disks and plates that grow up to the level of the water surface.

Seasonal rains may accumulate underground in salt pans, and form pools of extreme-hypersaline brine.

These ultra-salty pools may have extraordinary colours (such as bright green or yellow at Dallol, Ethiopia). They are often death traps for animals (such as migratory birds), which assume them to be freshwater, but die as soon as they ingest the toxic, ultra-concentrated brine.

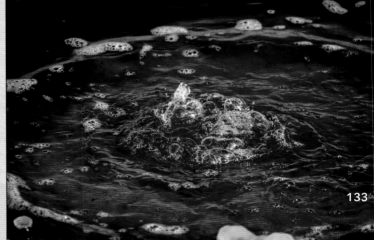

133

The repeated dissolving and reforming of surface layers of salt in salt pans results in some of the flattest landscapes on Earth.

Just one centimetre of rainfall may be enough to uniformly flood a salt pan, creating a reflective landscape that seemingly lacks a horizon.

Bolivia's Salar de Uyuni is the largest salt flat in the world. When it floods, if the water is only a few centimetres deep, it can give the impression of walking on water (especially when viewed from a distance).

The hypersaline nature of flooded salt pans generally prevents multi-cellular life from existing. However, there are a few exceptions. Brine shrimps (*Artemia* spp.) can survive in 25% salt solutions, and their populations can rapidly bloom when conditions are right.

Literally millions of brine shrimps can occur in a single cubic metre of brine. This abundance of food can attract a few highly specialised larger animals, such as flamingos which will congregate at flooded salt ponds to filter brine shrimps from the water, using their highly specialised beaks. It's the pink colouration of brine shrimps (and other food) that turns flamingos' feathers bright pink!

SULPHUR LANDSCAPES

Dallol is a hydrothermal region in the north of Ethiopia.

It is located in one of the deepest points within the Great Rift Valley, which is a gigantic gash in the African continent that is slowly expanding as the African tectonic plate is splitting apart.

Dallol has a negative altitude (down to -130 m below sea level) and is one of the lowest points of land on Earth.

It is also one of the hottest places on the planet (with temperatures up to 49°C recorded), and amongst the driest (several years can pass with no rainfall recorded)!

Within this extreme landscape, many hydrothermal vents splutter and hiss, as hot liquids (up to 100°C) reach the surface and evaporate, leaving encrustations of sulphur, salt and other minerals.

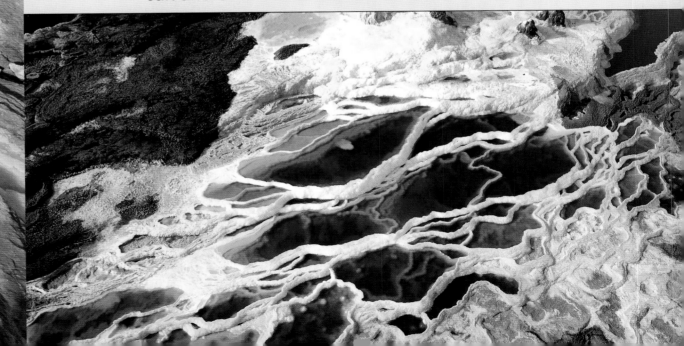

The landscape of Dallol is truly alien.

Pools of bright yellow, lime green and reddish brown sulphur-rich liquids accumulate in mineral terraces.

The liquid in the pools is hypersaline and highly acidic. Locals warn that it can severely burn skin, so you need to be extremely careful when exploring Dallol!

Much of the ground is covered with encrustations of sulphur, salt and iron, which can develop into unusual shapes including disks, pillars, flower-shaped crystals and hollow crusts that may be egg-shaped or spherical.

The minerals that make up the encrustations oxidise in air, and turn orange then reddish-brown as they age.

The hydrothermal activity of Dallol is continually changing, and this is shown in the colour of the minerals. Areas where the hydrothermal vents are inactive quickly loose their brilliant colours and turn brown.

Due to the amount of sulphur released by the hydrothermal activity, Dallol smells strongly of rotten eggs, and the pong can be so strong, that it may be smelt downwind many kilometres away!

Due to the extreme heat, salinity and toxicity, virtually no plants or animals can survive at Dallol.

SULPHUR FIRES

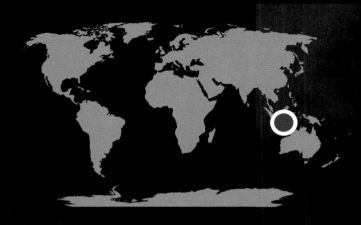

Many volcanoes and geothermal vents release concentrations of sulphur that accumulate as bright yellow deposits.

The Mount Ijen Volcano Complex on the Indonesian island of Java is famous for having sulphur vents that regularly catch on fire!

The sulphurous gases that emerge from the vents burn at over 600°C with eerie blue flames.

When large amounts of gas are released, the flames can reach many metres tall. The vents may also release liquid sulphur that trickles over the ground forming a stream of intense blue fire.

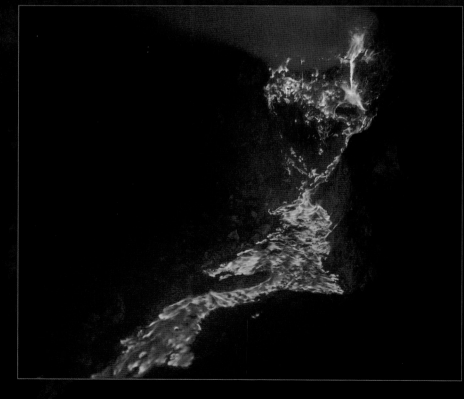

Sulphur has many industrial uses, and has been harvested from volcanoes for centuries. But collecting sulphur is one of the most dangerous jobs in the world!

Around 200 miners work on the Mount Ijen Volcano Complex. Twice a day, they climb up the volcano, dig sulphur from the vents, and carry up to 90 kg of sulphur at a time in wicker baskets on their shoulders.

The volcanic vents are unpredictable, and may splutter red-hot liquid sulphur or super-heated gas at any time.

It is also difficult to see the blue flames of burning sulphur during daylight, and the acidic fumes released from the vents are also dangerous to breathe.

After braving all of these hazards, each miner has to walk many kilometres to sell his load. Sometimes, the miners even work at night, under the eerie blue light of the sulphur fires (page 143)!

SULPHUR FIRES

VOLCANOES

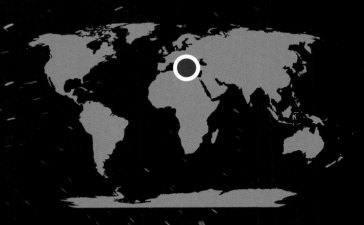

Volcanoes are places on the Earth's surface where underlying hot magma bursts through a weakness in the crust, spewing out molten lava. The lava slowly cools and solidifies, forming a cone shape to the volcano, which gradually grows in size if eruptions continue.

Volcanoes tend to occur along the boundaries of the Earth's tectonic plates. In some situations adjacent plates will be moving apart (known as divergence and present along mid-ocean ridges); while elsewhere they will be pushing against each other (known as convergence, as happens around the rim of the Pacific Ocean, or the 'Ring of Fire'). 75% of all the world's volcanoes occur along this 40,000 km, horseshoe-shaped Ring of Fire.

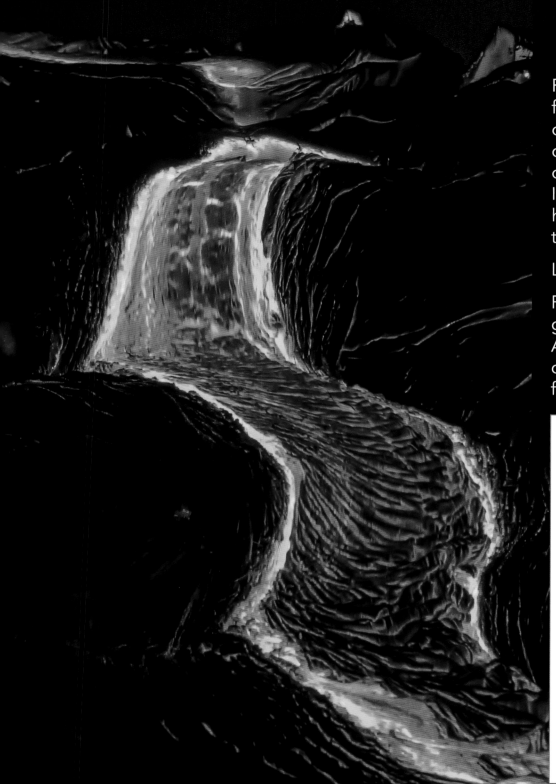

Red, yellow and even white-hot molten lava may form flows down the sides of some volcanoes from the point of eruption. The uppermost layer of these flows will cool and stabilse first, but hotter lava underneath will continue to move and force the flow to keep going. It takes many days, even weeks, after an eruption has ceased for the lava to have cooled down to the temperature of the surrounding rocks.

Lava flows aren't the only danger to be aware of!

Pyroclastic flows, consisting of hot rocks, ash and toxic gases can race down slopes at speeds of 450 mph. And volcanic mudlflows known as lahars can be very destructive too; as can volcanic ash, made up of sharp fragments of rocks and volcanic glass.

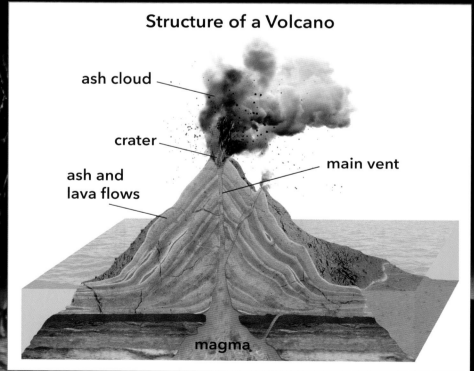

Structure of a Volcano

ash cloud

crater

main vent

ash and lava flows

magma

As many as 12 volcanoes occur every day and we rarely get to hear about any of them.

The vast majority of volcanoes erupt under the sea and most of us would not know they had occurred at all. It's only the large, spectacular ones which make the news.

Extinct volcanoes are those that scientists consider unlikely to erupt again because the volcano no longer has a magma supply. Edinburgh castle in Scotland famously sits on top of an extinct volcano.

Inactive volcanoes may be dormant rather than extinct, and telling the two states apart can be tricky, even for volcanologists. A volcano's state of dormancy may last hundreds of thousands of years before it starts to erupt again.

The ash which is released from volcanoes usually contains many minerals, and forms phosphorus and nitrogen-rich soils.

Volcanic soils may be so fertile that non-active volcanoes can become quickly covered in vegetation, such as the cone of the extinct volcano of Vayots Sar in Armenia (shown here). In tropical conditions, where water and warmth are abundant, lush forests may cover volcano cones within a few decades (e.g. the island of New Britain, Papua New Guinea).

While lava flows are generally dark grey or black, volcanic ash may be very varied in colour as a result of its differing chemical composition. Shades of red, orange, brown, white, grey and black are common. Each release of ash from a volcano may come out a different hue!

148

Sitting on top of the Kelimutu volcano on the island of Flores in Indonesia are three crater lakes. Each lake has its own colour due to a unique blend of chemicals released by the volcano. The lakes frequently change colour (sometimes overnight) when further minerals are released by geothermal activity, changing the water chemistry. Each lake may become white, brown, red or bright turquoise.

The loose nature of volcanic ash means that volcanoes may erode rapidly, often into dramatic shapes and contours. The photo below shows the Mount Bromo complex in Java, which remains active and continues to puff ash.

LAVA LAKES

Of the hundreds of active volcanoes scattered across the world, only eight have persistent lava lakes (pools of liquid lava that do not solidify).

The world's eight lava lakes of the world occur on:

Mount Erebus (Antarctica),
Mount Nyiragongo (DR Congo),
Erta Ale volcano (Ethiopia),
Kilauea volcano (Big Island, Hawaii),
Mount Masaya (Nicaragua),
Mount Michael (Saunders Isle, South Sandwich Islands),
Ambrym Island (Vanuatu),
Mount Yasur (Vanuatu).

The lava lake on Mount Michael was discovered as recently as 2019, by scientists from University College London and the British Antarctic Survey, who analysed satellite data and spotted glowing lava!

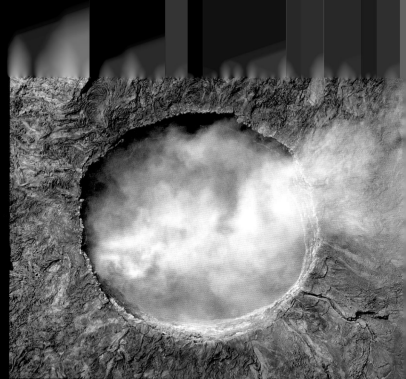

The lava lake of Erta Ale volcano, in the deserts of northern Ethiopia, is one of the world's most spectacular. It is also the longest-existing lake of lava known, having been documented since 1906.

Erta Ale is a gently rising shield volcano. Its summit stands at only 600 m or so high. However, within the volcano's caldera, there are multiple vents and two main pits which both variably contain lakes of lava.

Depending upon the pressure of underground magma, one or both of the pits may flood with lava. The pits are up to 90 m deep, and the lava has been known to overflow and form rivers of glowing liquid rock that drain through the caldera (as can be seen in the darker, more recent, flows in the top left photo).

Inside the pits, the lava glows bright orange and continually churns, as vents release super-heated gases and upwelling magma. The surface of the lava lake cools and solidifies, but the churning action of the lava means that sections of hardened 'crust' that form on the lake surface are continually broken and subducted under each other as they form (exactly like mini-tectonic plates). As such, the lava lake never completely solidifies.

During some years, activity is low, and the pits contain little lava and mostly belch gas and steam. However, the lava can return quickly, and with little warning. A major eruption in 2005 forced thousands of local farmers to flee and killed at least 250 goats and camels. In the local Afar language, Erta Ale means "smoking mountain", and the southernmost pit of the caldera is known locally as "the gateway to Hell"!

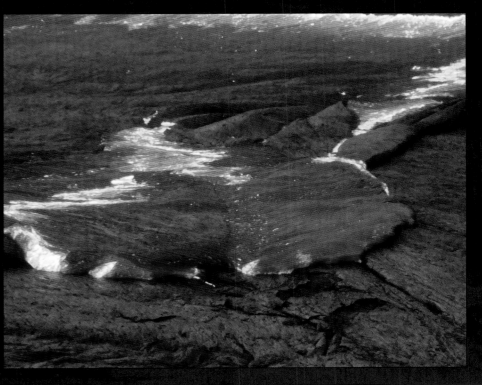

GATES OF HELL

The Karakum Desert in Turkmenistan, Central Asia, is an area that is very rich with natural gas.

In 1971, geologists from the Soviet Union began drilling for gas near to the village of Darvaza. Their drill broke into an underground chamber, and suddenly, the ground all around the drilling rig collapsed, leaving a crater-like hole around 70 m wide.

The geologists noticed a hissing sound, and discovered that gas was being released from the rocks in the crater.

They feared the gas could be poisonous and would build up, so they decided to set the crater on fire, believing the rocks would soon run out of gas.

Fifty years later, the gas is still being released from the rocks, and the crater is still burning, and no one knows when the underground gas supply will run out!

Locals have named the Darvaza crater the 'Gates of Hell', claiming that it resembles a door to the underworld!

The gas of the Darvaza crater is discharged from hundreds of vents in the rock, each visible by patches of flames. The fires never stop burning.

Even if the flames at a particular vent are extinguished (for example, by the wind), as the vent releases more gas, it soon bursts into flames again, reignited by one of the other burning vents nearby.

The firey scene is especially impressive at night, as the whole crater glows orange and red!

IMAGE CREDITS

The publisher and author would like to thank all those photographers and image makers who have contributed to this book.

SS = Shutterstock.

Front Endpaper Best-Backgrounds/SS; **Front Cover** Aphelleon/SS, WATHIT H/SS, Michail_Vorobyev/SS, emperorcosar/SS, matteo_it/SS, JamiesOnAMission/SS, Krissanapong Wongsawarng/SS, Wead/SS, sunsinger/SS, Kirill Trubitsyn/SS, alessandro pinto/SS; **1** T photography/SS, acarapi/SS, Danita Delmont/SS, Standret/SS, kavram/SS, emperorcosar/SS, Albert Russ/SS, Stewart McPherson; **2** Steve Heap/SS; **3** Itay.G/SS; **4** Danita Delmont/SS; **5** Itay.G/SS; **6** Aphelleon/SS; **7** AzmanMD/SS, acarapi/SS; **8** Digital Photo/SS, Diego Barucco/SS, Catmando/SS; **9** Willyam Bradberry/SS; **10** Photography by SC/SS; **11** Steffen Foerster/SS, Soft Lighting/SS, YuRi Photolife/SS, Herschel Hoffmeyer/SS; **12** Rost9/SS; **13** Vitamin/SS, Arcady/SS, thoron/SS, R. de Bruijn_Photography/SS; **14** Aphelleon/SS, Allgord/SS, Denis Burdin/SS; **15** Photodynamic/SS, Tomarchio Francesco/SS, Ase/SS; **16** Denis Belitsky/SS; **17** Denis Belitsky/SS, Krissanapong Wongsawarng/SS; **18** Corepics VOF/SS, Sylvie Corriveau/SS; **19** Guitar photographer/SS, Denis Belitsky/SS; **20** Christos Kotsiopoulos; **21** Christos Kotsiopoulos, valdezrl/SS; **22** Nosdois/SS, Francisco Negroni/Alamy Stock Photo; **23** AB Forces News Collection/Alamy Stock Photo, Svet_Feo/SS, Mario Hagen/SS; **24** kavram/SS; **25** kavram/SS, Sourav and Joyeeta/SS; **26** canadastock/SS, Bill45/SS, ESB Professional/SS; **27** CAN BALCIOGLU/SS, Heide Hellebrand/SS, M.Ellinger/SS, puttsk/SS; **28** Lukas Gojda/SS; **29** Lukas Gojda/SS, Belikova Oksana/SS; **30** iPics/SS; **31** Edward Graden/SS, Davidolfi/SS, Yulia_Bogomolova/SS; **32** Daniel Sockwell/SS, Erik AJV/SS, Donna Carpenter/SS; **33** Erika Bisbocci/SS, Iurii Kazakov/SS, Danita Delmont/SS; **34** Annonymous/SS; **35** Annonymous/SS, Arnaud Payan/SS; **36** Leah-Anne Thompson/SS, Emre Dikici/SS, Arnaud Payan/SS; **37** tonkid/SS, Ting Cheng/SS; **38** JC Photo/SS; **39** JC Photo/SS, Ingvars Birznieks/SS; **40** JamiesOnAMission/SS; **41** JamiesOnAMission/SS, Angelo Giampiccolo/SS; **42** David A Knight/SS; **43** David A Knight/SS, David A Knight/SS; **44** David A Knight/SS, kid315/SS; **45** XU GENG/SS, Charles Brewer-Carias; **46** footageclips/SS; **47** footageclips/SS, Alexander Pink/SS; **48** Kriveart90/SS, Eyem/SS, Stephen Moehle/SS; **49** kanta_kulat/SS, Charles Leonard/SS, David A Knight/SS; **50** Javier Trueba/MSF/Science Photo Library; **51** Javier Trueba/MSF/Science Photo Library; **52** Javier Trueba/MSF/Science Photo Library; **53** Javier Trueba/MSF/Science Photo Library; **54** Shaun Jeffers/SS; **55** Shaun Jeffers/SS; **56** Marcel Strelow/SS, Matej Halouska/SS; **57** Lin4pic/SS, Leandro Reichert/SS; **58** Denis Burdin/SS; **59** Denis Burdin/SS, Andrea Willmore/SS; **60** Daniel Andis/SS, Luke Wait/SS; **61** Johan Swanepoel/SS, LUC KOHNEN/SS, DONGHYEOK KWON/SS, Peter Fodor/SS, Radek Borovka/SS; **62** Roberto Caucino/SS, Mark Green/SS, trevor kittelty/SS; **63** soft_light/SS, Oleg Znamenskiy/SS; **64** Benny Marty/SS; **65** Benny Marty/SS, jared ropelato/SS; **66** Michael Andrew Just/SS, VectorMine/SS; **67** EQRoy/SS, Jakub Barzycki/SS; **68** Danita Delmont/SS; **69** Danita Delmont/SS, MeganBrady/SS; **70** Filip Fuxa/SS, Krishna.Wu/SS; **71** Dancestrokes/SS, Harry Beugelink/SS; **72** naoima/SS, WAB Studio/SS; **73** Joshua Davenport/SS, GUDKOV ANDREY/SS, slowmotiongli/SS; **74** Mikhail Priakhin/SS; **75** Mikhail Priakhin/SS, Bas van den Heuvel/SS; **76** Ugu/SS, Karin Wassmer/SS; **77** In Green/SS; **78** sunsinger/SS; **79** sunsinger/SS, KPG_Payless/SS; **80** Vadim Petrakov; **81** godi photo/SS, Dietmar Temps/SS; **82** Standret/SS; **83** Standret/SS, Lukaschevich Sergei/SS; **84** Aslinah Safar/SS, White_Fox/SS; **85** Pixelcruiser/SS, Sergey Pesterev/SS; **86** Nicolaj Larsen/SS; **87** Nicolaj Larsen/SS, Armin Rose/SS; **88** Henri Vandelanotte/SS, Romolo Tavani/SS, William Ng; **89** FloridaStock/SS, Alexey Seafarer/SS, Eric Lew, Stephen Lew/SS; **90** Wikipedia/National Science Foundation/Peter Rejcek; **91** Wikipedia/National Science Foundation/Peter Rejcek; **92** Albert Russ/SS; **93** Albert Russ/SS, Kris Grabiec/SS; **94** DCrane/SS; **95** MAGNIFIER/SS, Nadezda Murmakova/SS; **96** Colin Harris/era-images/Alamy Stock Photo;

97 Colin Harris/era-images/Alamy Stock Photo, John Carnemolla/SS; 98 Colin Harris/era-images/Alamy Stock Photo; 99 Dale Lorna Jacobsen/SS, Sean M Smith/SS; 100 Stewart McPherson; 101 Stewart McPherson; 102 Stewart McPherson; 103 Stewart McPherson/ Antonio Hitcher; 104 Stewart McPherson/ Antonio Hitcher; 105 Stewart McPherson/SS, Vladimir Melnik/SS; 106 Nikolas_jkd/SS; 107 Nikolas_jkd/SS, Grindstone Media Group/SS; 108 muratart/SS; 109 muratart/SS, Suksamran1985/SS; 110 clkraus/SS, Vadim Petrakov/SS; 111 michel arnault/SS, Stewart McPherson/SS; 112 Greg Brave/SS; 113 Greg Brave/SS; 114 Zhukova Valentyna/SS; 115 Zhukova Valentyna/SS, Stefano Borsa/SS; 116 Ernest Safaryan/SS, Kayla Crouch/SS; 117 Johnny Adolphson/SS, Paul Brady Photography/SS; 118 Nagel Photography/SS; 119 Nagel Photography/SS, Natalia Bratslavsky/SS; 120 Reiner Conrad/SS, POZZO DI BORGO Thomas/SS; 121 michel arnault/SS, Pierre-Yves Babelon/SS; 122 matteo_it/SS; 123 matteo_it/SS, len4foto/SS; 124 Siarhei Liudkevich/SS, Phassa K/SS; 125 Pranch/SS, Bikomins/SS; 126 alessandro pinto/SS; 127 alessandro pinto/SS, Daniel Prudek/SS; 128 Jcking3/SS, caioacquesta/SS; 129 Yerbolat Shadrakhov/SS; 130 T photography/SS; 131 T photography/SS, Marieke Funke/SS; 132 Stewart McPherson; 133 wuthrich didier/SS, Radek Borovka/SS, mikluha_maklai/SS, Tanguy de Saint-Cyr/SS; 134 Benedikt Juerges/SS, Vadim Petrakov/SS; 135 Napat/SS, Peter Wollinga/SS, andreanord/SS; 136 Kirill Trubitsyn/SS; 137 Kirill Trubitsyn/SS, Stewart McPherson; 138 Radek Borovka/SS, Tanguy de Saint-Cyr/SS; 139 yggdrasill/SS, Manamana/SS, Vladislav Belchenko/SS; 140 Mazur Travel/SS; 141 Mazur Travel/SS, MemoryMan/SS; 142 Putu Artana/SS, R.M. Nunes/Alamy Stock Photo, Sponsorchen/SS; 143 robertharding/Alamy Stock Photo, mauritius images GmbH/Alamy Stock Photo, cesc_assawin/SS; 144 Wead/SS; 145 Wead/SS, Deni_Sugandi/SS; 146 Yvonne Baur/SS, Aldona Griskeviciene/SS; 147 Yvonne Baur/SS, Willyam Bradberry/SS; 148 Zaven Sargsyan/SS, aapsky/SS, mass911/SS; 149 Muhammad Nurudin/SS, Manamana/SS; 150 Michail_Vorobyev/SS; 151 Michail_Vorobyev/SS, Fredy Thuerig/SS; 152 Stewart McPherson; 153 yggdrasill/SS, Yury S. Petrov/SS, Mikhail Cheremkin/SS; 154 Matyas Rehak/SS; 155 Matyas Rehak/SS, Iwanami Photos/SS; 156 Matt Amery/SS, Dankc Adventure/SS; 157 Matt Amery/SS, Ed Berlen/SS: 159 Brad Wilson; **Back Endpaper** Best-Backgrounds/SS.

THE AUTHOR

Stewart McPherson is a British naturalist, author and film-maker. He spent ten years climbing 300 mountains across the world to study and photograph carnivorous plants to write a series of 30 books. Along the way, he co-discovered and co-named 35 new species/varieties including some of the largest carnivorous pitcher plants ever found.

Between 2012 and 2015, Stewart and a camera team travelled to all of the UK Overseas Territories to film the *Britain's Treasure Islands* documentary series for BBC and SBS. The accompanying book was distributed widely, and sponsored copies were donated to 5,350 schools and 2,000 libraries.

In 2019, Stewart worked closely with the Don Hanson Charitable Foundation to create and donate boxes of educational resources to 10,000 schools across the UK to inspire students' learning and passion for conservation.

In 2020, he worked with the Don Hanson Charitable Foundation and the Jane Goodall Institute Australia to send boxes of resources to 20,000 schools across the UK and 4,000 schools across Australia.

www.stewartmcpherson.com

IMAGE CREDITS

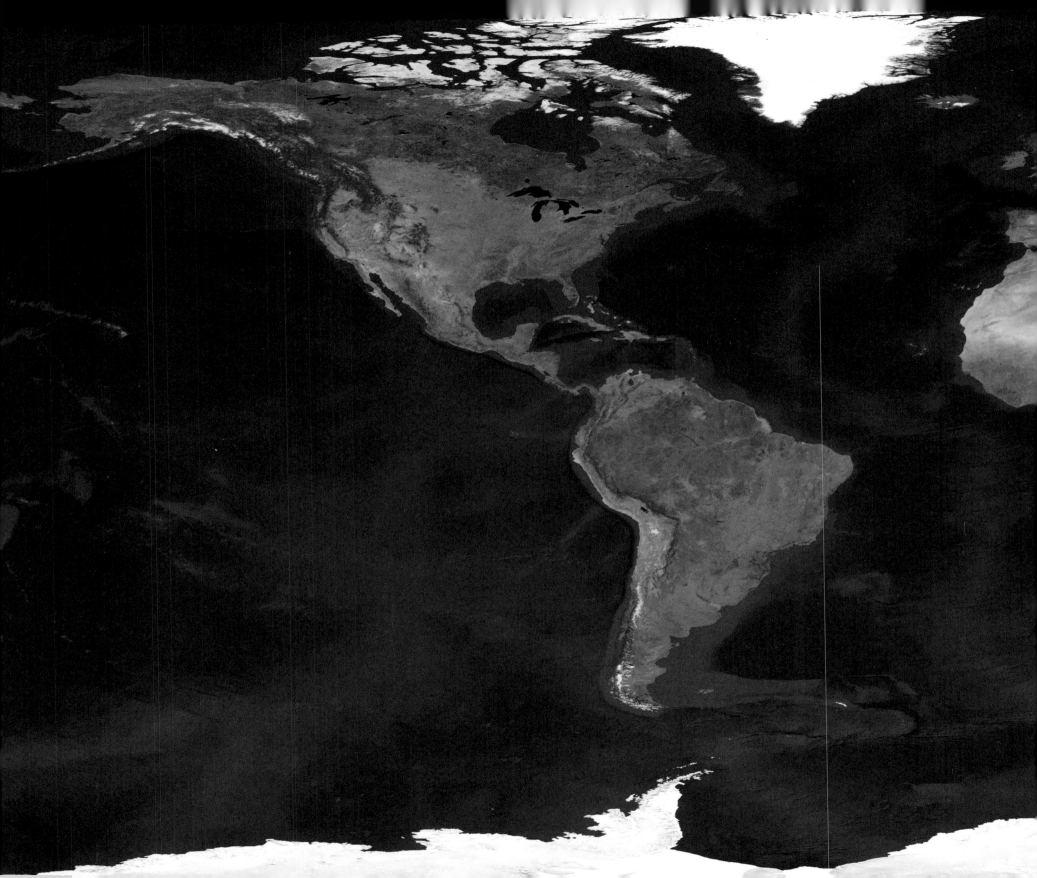